M000291360

In honour of the element of water for without it, we would not exist.

'MAY ALL WATER ON THE PLANET BE PURIFIED'

I'M SO GRATEFUL YOU FOUND MY DIARY!

....

....

....

GIVING THANKS

Welcome

Here we are – 2024 and the 15th edition of the Gratitude Diary! I'm pinching myself as I reflect that time moves SOOO fast.

If you are new to my book, WELCOME! Thank you for trusting the synchronicity that drew you to the DIVINE mermaid on the cover... and for purchasing this diary. If you are a returning reader, an even bigger THANK YOU. It is your loyalty that allows me to continue to publish our beautiful journal, which is produced with so much soul and good intent.

I remember the state I was in when I initially conceived the idea for this Gratitude Diary back in 2009. The best way I can describe how I felt was 'all at sea'. I was lost – in deep murky grey underwaters – unsure of what actions I needed to take to move forward. Yet, from ever since I can remember, I'd also been waiting... anticipating something miraculous that I knew was going to make my soul grow... and it did!

The miracle was GRATITUDE. The simple, yet profound practice of Giving Thanks. My soul moved forward and no longer resides at the bottom of the murky ocean. I continue to grow. The current does not stay still. This is the natural order of life. Movement, progression, in and out, ups and downs. Good and bad. The Leyla.

'At sea' has inspired the theme of WATER for this year's Gratitude Diary. My motivation has been to connect more deeply with water. I'm surrounded by it down here in Tasmania. Massive, healthy flowing rivers, oceans as far as the eye can see, snow, fog, frost on the grass... And of course, there are the creatures whose home is the sea, including our ancient custodians, the whales and dolphins, as well as the entire ecosystem that supports life under our watery realms...

There is, of course, a shadow side to acknowledge here too. When we connect to, and understand more deeply, the element of water, we must also recognise and be accountable for water pollution. In this year's Diary I've questioned some of our fish farming practices, mainly our Salmon industry and the problems it causes for other sea creatures, particularly whales and dolphins. I've evoked the fairy of our oceans – the mermaids – and invited them to the table for a conversation.

At the time of writing this, I'm right in the end stages of the planet Chiron's return in my astrological birth chart. Chiron is a small planet that orbits our solar system, full circle every 50 years. He is our wounded healer archetype; the part of us that assists others in order to balance karma within ourself. It's a long time between his visits but his return provides the opportunity for us to ask what is motivating our beliefs, thoughts and actions. I'm wondering now if it is Chiron's energy that activates the mid-life crisis in our society? Learn about the conversation you might have with Chiron when he makes his return in your own life.

I do not need to mention (but I will) the intense times of change we are living through. What my Chiron return has brought home to me is this: If we are motivated by fear we will continue to create more fear – but if love is our motivation, love is the lighthouse that will guide us, not only through this storm, but to a new cleaner earth with pristine oceans, seas and waterways.

May your year be blessed with love and grace,

x Melanie

IF I AM IN THE NORTHERN HEMISPHERE WILL MY FRIEND IN THE SOUTHERN HEMISPHERE HAVE THE SAME EXPERIENCES ON THE NEW MOON?

This is a question we are frequently asked – let's see if the following information helps:

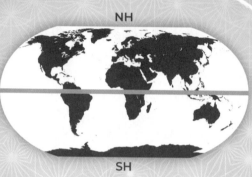

The Northern Hemisphere **(NH)** is everywhere above the equator; including Canada, America, United Kingdom, Europe, Asia, etc.

The Southern Hemisphere **(SH)** is everywhere below the equator; including Australia, New Zealand, South Africa & South America, etc.

Our experience of the New Moon will be coloured by what season and environment that we're in – but the overarching experience is worldwide.

Contemplate the vast distances that separate us from the other planets! In astrology we pay attention to the angles that the planets form in relationship to one another. These are called aspects and they inform us as to what tone a conversation may be taking. It takes two or more planets to form an aspect.

A New Moon occurs when the Sun and the Moon are on the same degree of any given point of the Zodiac. This aspect is called a conjunction. It's intimate and conversational. Like when we meld with another and can read each other's thoughts and feelings.

Where a conjunction occurs is also telling. Each of the twelve Zodiac signs has its own unique viewpoint and we get to experience a New Moon and make our intentions, coloured by each of these twelve perspectives over the course of the year.

Table of Contents

Thank you, Team

MELISSA WILLIAMS: Melissa's artistic capacity continues to evolve year after year and I am so proud to have her on our team. Melissa is skilled in the creative process of turning abstract ideas and musings from me into powerful, activating images that convey the message of Gratitude to our cellular bodies. Thank you, darling Melissa, for being you!
@misprintart | misprint.com.au

STEPHANIE CRANE: Steph, thank you for your grounded competency and love for this work. Deep acknowledgement and reverence for your ability to create not one, but two Diaries this year – all whilst being such a dedicated mum. Steph's wisdom and patience are beyond her years on this planet. And for this, I am truly grateful!
@sleepyhollowcreative

LEE BUCHANAN: For the third year now, Lee has been our Editor-in-Chief. A big heartfelt thank you as well to Alan for his second pair of eyes and for supporting Lee. You both work seamlessly together, helping to create intelligent order from my ramblings. This year has been particularly challenging and I have needed you more than ever. What stars you both are!
@millymaker

DEE HOLAS: Dee contacted me back in 2020 just to thank me for the Gratitude Diary. Dee also graciously offered to support our editing process as a gift from her heart. Since then she has been working away quietly in the background. Dee, your generosity and contributions have been invaluable and I consider you an integral part of our Gratitude Diary family. Thank you for being such an angel! deerose750@gmail.com

LISA WHITING: Giving Thanks is continually evolving and this process is supported by the passionate fire inside Lisa, our Business Operations Manager (my BOM!). With your loving support and unlimited belief in what we can achieve, the Gratitude Diary now has an online presence that matches the frequency of our printed journal. Lisa, you make all this and so much more possible and I love you dearly.

ARIEL KOROBACZ: Such an ongoing pleasure to have this amazing moon woman in my life! Ariel is an astrologer, potter, painter, and the wise author and voice of the Gratitude Diary's 'Moon Talks'. I'm very proud to add that together Ariel and I manifested the Astro Diary, which is now in her second year of print. This is only the beginning of our creative adventures together! auroafae.com

CHRISSIE HUGHES: Chrissie, you have been with our Gratitude Family since 2016 and have witnessed so many ongoing transformations of our Diary through your social media expertise. I know that you have also been on your own transformative journey, which I would like to honour. Together, while we have grown our businesses, we have grown ourselves. I hope you are with us for many more years to come, taking your delicious photographs, because you make us all shine!

The Quantum Power of Gratitude

5-DAY RETREAT WITH MELANIE SPEARS

FRIDAY 16th–THURSDAY 22nd AUGUST 2024
BYRON BAY NSW

*Are you ready to untangle patterns
that are holding you back
from stepping into the truth of who you are?*

This retreat will empower you to heal your past
And choose soul-alignment.

Featuring a world-class program with Melanie Spears that includes
daily facilitated Gratitude and Family Constellation workshops,
plus deep soul activation sessions with guest facilitators.
The retreat venue is located on an incredibly sacred site near magical Byron Bay,
and includes full catering of deeply nourishing foods.

*Realign to your true life path
using the power of Gratitude*

BOOK ONLINE
melaniespears.com/retreat

ARCHAEOLOGY OF THE SOUL

Soul mentoring with Melanie

Join me and fellow gratitude enthusiasts for a 12 month journey into the deep soul state of acceptance and gratitude.

Opening Ceremony Thursday 11th January 2024:

- Learn how to use your diary to achieve lasting emotional transformation.
- Understand why living with intent is key to achieving happiness in your life.
- Navigate and fine tune your 4 bodies (MIND, BODY, SPIRIT & SOUL).
- Connect and network professionally with other empaths and light workers.
- Share your wisdom and vulnerability inside a safe and supportive community.

YOUR SOUL IS SACRED.
YOUR EVOLUTION IS EXPECTED.

I am honoured to be your personal way-shower and friend... telling stories and letting stories go. x Melanie

BOOK ONLINE
melaniespears.mykajabi.com/archaeologyofthesoul

7

Yearly Planner

JANUARY

FEBRUARY

MARCH

APRIL

MAY

JUNE

....

....

....

2024

JULY

AUGUST

SEPTEMBER

OCTOBER

NOVEMBER

DECEMBER

Mind, Body, Spirit & Soul

AND WHAT'S THE DIFFERENCE?

Back in 2018, I introduced the Mind | Body | Spirit | Soul pages in the Gratitude Diary. My intention at the time was to encourage your journaling process into the contemplation of these four aspects of your being. So that it might carve even deeper awareness-pathways in your brain and therefore more understanding of the nature of YOU.

I see these four aspects as quite separate BODIES: our Human Body, our Mind Body, our Spirit Body, and our Soul Body. Who knew we had four bodies! I was not prepared for the reaction these pages stirred. Receiving week after week, letters from many readers wanting to know more. At the end of this article I have included some questions I was asked and my intuitive answers.

THE HUMAN BODY

You have probably got a handle on this one. Although have you considered that your body, just like your soul and spirit, is a separate entity? Think of your body as an astronaut's suit for this lifetime. You need your body in order to function, however once your body has retired and you have 'passed on', you will still be you – just without your suit.

While you are in your body in this/your lifetime, you need to take care of the body. We need to treat our body well with good nutrition, rest and regular 'service inspections' and 'safety checks'. Care of your body comes from LOVE. The more deeply you love your own Soul, the more deeply you will understand the moods and seasons of your body.

THE MIND BODY

Housed in your brain, the mind is a part of your Physical Body, yet is powered by all the other bodies.

The wonderful thing about the Mind Body is that it is a hard drive that is always upgrading to allow for new programs. Get clean with your mind by transporting into your higher self for a moment. Your Mind Body can be supported by your Human body with good nutrition, exercise and sleep; by your Spirit Body by being aware of the influences, frequencies or energy sources you are choosing to align with; and by your Soul, which is the source of everything, by being eternally grateful for your life.

THE SPIRIT BODY

The Spirit Body is sometimes referred to as an aura. I like to think of my Spirit body as that which houses my frequency or the resonance that I am vibrating at. If I am an electrical system (and we are!) – am I tuned in to high, medium or low frequencies? The Spirit Body has two very important functions. Firstly, while you are here on earth, the Spirit Body will provide the energy to your physical body. Secondly, the Spirit Body will continue to house your soul after death.

THE SOUL BODY

The Soul is the spiritual or immaterial part of us regarded as being immortal. The soul is what gives life to the body and is the totality of who you are at the human level – it is your authentic Self. To nourish your soul; practice gratitude (for everything), spend time in nature, be compassionate to yourself and to others, find your purpose for being here, and find ways to connect with something greater than yourself.

GOOD QUESTIONS

I have distilled the letters I received on this topic into the discussion below. Here are some of the most common questions and my intuitive responses:

Q1: WHAT'S THE DIFFERENCE BETWEEN MY SPIRIT AND MY SOUL?

I have always felt I had a spirit, although not sure about my soul, or what the difference is?

What a great question this is! Perhaps this is a common reality for most people.

A: The Spirit has a body, otherwise known as your AURIC FIELD. It is the light energy that encapsulates your physical body as you go about your day-to-day life. The Spirit Body can be visible to the human eye, and usually can be seen as frequencies of colour.

I remember opening my eyes from a group meditation to notice the facilitator walking quietly across the room, followed by a pillow-sized purple hue trailing behind his head. For the first time in my life, I had seen an aura.

The Spirit Body is the 'Divineness' of you. It is the energy system that remains universal, and therefore intimately connected to source energy – your BRIDGE to something greater. It is something unified and complete in, and of, itself. Your soul, however, is more personal. It is your library, your memories, experiences, trials, lessons, wounds, desires, hopes and dreams. Your Soul, in essence, is where YOU reside. So like a crab, your soul dwells inside the shell of your Spirit Body.

Q2: WHY IS THERE SO LITTLE INFORMATION ABOUT THE SOUL?

I have often wondered about that myself.

For example, here in Australia, we have the Mind Body Spirit festival – With no 'Soul' in the title!

We have the new age spiritual movement – Again no 'Soul'.

The Soul has been very much underrated over the last few thousand years.

A: I began my Journey with Soul back in 2009. I found Gary Zukav's book, 'The Seat of the Soul', and could not put it down. I then went on to read Lynne Twist's book, 'The Soul of Money', and was equally activated. I drew the conclusion that, in some weird way, the Soul in society had been suppressed along with the divine feminine who went underground for many centuries. Yet as she rises so does the memory of the soul. OR is the feminine rising because collectively souls are waking up? "Tomato, tomatoe."

You will notice SOUL everywhere. Soul lives in the stories, the movies, and in the music. Soul moves you in unexplained ways. Soul gives you motivation and direction, purpose and drive. Soul is perhaps the REASON you get up every day. Soul is the lighthouse, constantly beckoning you towards her, singing your song.

Q3: WHAT AM I SUPPOSED TO BE JOURNALING ABOUT MY MIND?

A: Well, how is your mind behaving? How are your own thoughts treating you? Do you have soothing words for yourself, words of encouragement and support?

OR do you have a negative script running through your mind that is dictating your motivation levels during daylight?

How do you use your mind? Do you analyse and judge people incessantly, or even sometimes? Are you critical towards others' choices.

Most importantly, are you critical towards YOURSELF.

Get clean with your own mind by transporting into your higher self for a moment, and taking a mind assessment. What is going on here?

Q4: WHAT KIND OF QUESTIONS DO I ASK MY BODY?

A: Your body, just like your soul and spirit, is an entity. In other words, your body is not you. You NEED your body in order to function, however once your body has retired, you will still be you. We must maintain regular service inspections and safety checks. Care of your body comes from LOVE. Plus the more deeply you love your own soul, the more deeply you will understand the moods and seasons of your body. Here are some good enquiry prompts.

Speak AS yourself when you ask the questions. Respond as YOUR BODY.

A CONVERSATION WITH MY BODY

Body, do you feel WELL treated by me? How could I be treating you BETTER?

....

....

....

....

....

Body, what kind of NUTRITION best supports and maintains you?
What should I be feeding you MORE of?

....

....

....

....

....

Body, are you happy with the amount of REST I am providing you?
What ways can I offer you more support?

....

....

....

....

....

January

S	M	T	W	T	F	S
31	1	2	3	4	5	6
7	8	9	10	11	12	13
14	15	16	17	18	19	20
21	22	23	24	25	26	27
28	29	30	31	1	2	3

IMPORTANT THINGS TO DO

PERSONAL GOALS

SEEDING MY DREAMING

BIRTHDAYS

Giving thanks every day

MONDAY 1st JANUARY

Giving thanks every day

....

....

....

....

....

....

....

....

....

....

....

....

....

THE MIND AND BODY

ARE NOT SEPARATE ENTITIES.

They are intimately connected and interdependent.

MAHATMA GANDHI

Giving thanks every day
WEDNESDAY 3rd JANUARY

....
....
....
....
....
....
....
....
....
....
....
....
....
....
....
....
....
....
....

Giving thanks every day

THURSDAY 4th JANUARY

....
....
....
....
....
....
....
....
....
....
....
....
....

THE SPIRIT IS THE BREATH OF THE SOUL,

and the body is the vessel that carries both.

FRIEDRICH NIETZSCHE

Giving thanks every day

FRIDAY 5th JANUARY

....

....

....

....

....

....

....

....

....

....

....

....

....

....

....

....

....

....

....

....

Giving thanks every day

SATURDAY 6th JANUARY

....
....
....
....
....
....
....
....

SUNDAY 7th JANUARY

....
....
....
....
....
....
....

Giving thanks every day

MONDAY 8th JANUARY

....

....

....

....

....

....

....

....

....

....

....

....

....

....

....

....

....

....

Giving thanks every day

TUESDAY 9th JANUARY

....
....
....
....
....
....
....
....
....
....
....
....

THE SOUL IS THE DIVINE SPARK WITHIN US,

connecting us to the eternal realm of existence.

PLATO

25

Giving thanks every day
WEDNESDAY 10th JANUARY

Giving thanks every day

....

....

NEW MOON IN CAPRICORN

NH 11.01.24 SH 11.01.24

Capricorn is the sign of achievement and success. Here, the Sun highlights ambitions – Who do you want to be in the World? Which ladder do you need to scale, mountain goat like, to achieve the best overview? For the one with the clearest vision, who keeps an eye on the prize, and on the competition, has the greatest likelihood of success.

When the Moon is in Capricorn, she is extremely pragmatic – it is not that she does not have feelings – more that she is willing to put them aside to achieve her goals. She is strong and can endure the long game.

If you are feeling an added intensity, that may be Pluto you are picking up on. Pluto stirs up powerful emotions and plays power games. Thankfully, this Capricorn Moon will help to keep us grounded and mission focused.

The South and North Node are also of influence, forming a tight square. When the Nodes are involved, we can feel the nostalgic pull of the past, and excitement, with a touch of panic, as to what the future holds – and also, if we have what it takes to meet it successfully.

This is a powerful New Moon for intentions focused on any area where you feel responsible and are carrying responsibility. This could be in business, career, and long-term goals. Or it might be managing your family's finances and dreams of home

NEW MOON
Intentions

THURSDAY 11th JANUARY

....

....

....

....

....

....

....

Where do you feel responsible?

Where can you let responsibility go?

Find the Balance.

CAPRICORN

MIND

....

....

....

....

....

BODY

....

....

....

....

....

SPIRIT

....

....

....

....

....

SOUL

....

....

....

....

....

Gratitude as Devotional Practice

BY ERIN LEE

When I first began practicing Gratitude I remember *doing* it, as though it was some sort of checklist about what was going well in my life. It felt good to direct my mind towards the positive, and I thought that was the extent of what giving thanks was.

However some years later a rather unpleasant life event unfolded, revealing the deeper power of Gratitude.

My husband, and father of our two young daughters, died suddenly. On one breath we were walking and talking; on the next he was lying on the ground unconscious, declared dead soon after. After months of medical investigations, no medical cause of death could be determined.

HOW CAN I BE GRATEFUL WHEN I'M IN GRIEF?

There was little room for Gratitude in a 'positive thinking' sense, in those early days without my love. I was far too consumed with the shock, disbelief, grief and anger about the unfairness of it all. My mind swung between the past and the future, desperately trying to grasp onto a reason for it happening, whilst at the same time working out strategies for my future as a single parent.

Some weeks into my new life without Nico, I started seeing a mindfulness therapist. In our first session she guided me through a body scan meditation – an invitation to become aware of the physical sensations in my body.

It was then that I felt it:

Presence.

My mind released past and future thinking and landed in 'the now'.

But what I found was not pleasant!

I suddenly became aware of *all* my resistance: the tension in my neck and shoulders, the shallowness of my breath, the armour around my heart; the way I was holding it all together.

The tears poured. I felt unsteady and shaky.

Yet in that same moment of Presence, I felt a deep acceptance of everything in life – *including a momentary acceptance of what had happened to my husband.*

A new way of practicing Gratitude had revealed itself.

GRATITUDE LIVES IN THE NOW

Gratitude is not just about giving thanks for what is going well... It is a deep acceptance and *honouring* of what is here in this present moment.

You can not force acceptance; it unfolds through releasing any resistance to what is.

As a result, the awareness broadens, the senses expand, and we begin to notice the finer details of life again – now that we are no longer consumed by the immediate emotions and thoughts that come with unpleasant events.

GRATITUDE IS NOT A POSITIVE AFFIRMATION

Wishing for things to be well is an empty gesture, without an acceptance of how things actually are.

All these years later, I reflect back on my grieving self in those early days following Nico's death... Of course, Gratitude felt so inaccessible because I was coming at it with an existing resistance. It was not until I became aware of my resistance, that the resistance dissolved. In the absence of resistance, Gratitude began to naturally grow.

Of course, I did not feel joyous about Nico's death, however what I did feel was an acceptance that 'it is what it is'. There was no need to mentally construct things to be grateful for about the event; Gratitude was an act of being present with the event.

This is why reeling off a list of things that you are grateful for, without first acknowledging how things are, falls flat.

Gratitude is not an action; rather it is a quality or an attitude that envelops us when we fully surrender ourselves to the existence of what is.

BECOMING DEVOTIONAL

When we make Gratitude a devotional practice, we honour life – all of it, the pleasant and the unpleasant – by offering our full Presence to what is here.

We allow life to be.

In turn, the struggle dissolves.

It does not mean the event was ok, however it makes everything we are feeling about the event ok.

The moment that we give our full awareness to our aching back, our breaking heart, and our tired body, is the moment that we offer our presence and aliveness to life as it exists in THIS moment.

This is what makes Gratitude a devotional practice.

This way of practicing Gratitude has supported me to make peace with my husband's death, as much as it has connected me to his divine, eternal existence.

AN INVITATION:
Allow yourself to meet with what exists in this present moment.
Deeply accept how things are right now.
It does not mean they will be like this forever...
Loosen your grip on life, and open to the whisper of Gratitude:
"I acknowledge you; I honour you and I devote my presence to your existence."

x Erin Lee

Giving thanks every day

Giving thanks every day

SATURDAY 13th JANUARY

....

....

....

....

....

....

....

....

SUNDAY 14th JANUARY

....

....

....

....

....

....

....

Giving thanks every day

MONDAY 15th JANUARY

Giving thanks every day

TUESDAY 16th JANUARY

....
....
....
....
....
....
....
....
....
....
....
....

If a relationship is not flourishing,

ASK IF THERE IS ENOUGH GRATITUDE

IN THE SOIL?

KERRY HOWELLS

Giving thanks every day

WEDNESDAY 17th JANUARY

....

....

....

....

....

....

....

....

....

....

....

....

....

....

....

....

....

....

....

....

....

....

Giving thanks every day

THURSDAY 18th JANUARY

....
....
....
....
....
....
....
....
....
....
....

Gratitude grows naturally

IN THE ABSENCE OF RESISTANCE.

Giving thanks every day

FRIDAY 19th JANUARY

....

....

....

....

....

....

....

....

....

....

....

....

....

....

....

....

....

Giving thanks every day

SATURDAY 20th JANUARY

....
....
....
....
....
....
....
....

SUNDAY 21st JANUARY

....
....
....
....
....
....
....
....

Giving thanks every day

MONDAY 22nd JANUARY

Giving thanks every day

TUESDAY 23rd JANUARY

....
....
....
....
....
....
....
....
....
....
....

You cannot force acceptance:

IT UNFOLDS THROUGH

RELEASING ANY RESISTANCE

TO WHAT IS.

Giving thanks every day

WEDNESDAY 24th JANUARY

Giving thanks every day

THURSDAY 25th JANUARY

Giving thanks every day

How are your intentions coming to fruition?

....

....

....

....

....

....

....

....

....

....

....

....

....

....

....

....

NH 25.01.24 SH 26.01.24

Giving thanks every day

SATURDAY 27th JANUARY

....
....
....
....
....
....
....
....

SUNDAY 28th JANUARY

....
....
....
....
....
....
....

Giving thanks every day

MONDAY 29th JANUARY

Giving thanks every day

TUESDAY 30th JANUARY

....
....
....
....
....
....
....
....
....
....
....
....

Gratitude

IS MORE THAN

A POSITIVE AFFIRMATION.

Giving thanks every day
WEDNESDAY 31st JANUARY

IMPORTANT THINGS TO DO

....

....

....

....

....

....

....

....

PERSONAL GOALS

....

....

....

....

SEEDING MY DREAMING

....

....

....

....

BIRTHDAYS

....

....

....

February

S	M	T	W	T	F	S
27	28	29	31	1	2	3
4	5	6	7	8	9	10
11	12	13	14	15	16	17
18	19	20	21	22	23	24
25	26	27	28	29	2	3

Giving thanks every day

THURSDAY 1st FEBRUARY

Giving thanks every day

FRIDAY 2nd FEBRUARY

....

....

....

....

....

....

....

....

....

....

....

....

....

....

....

....

....

Giving thanks every day

SATURDAY 3rd FEBRUARY

....
....
....
....
....
....
....
....

SUNDAY 4th FEBRUARY

....
....
....
....
....
....
....
....

Giving thanks every day

MONDAY 5th FEBRUARY

Giving thanks every day

TUESDAY 6th FEBRUARY

....
....
....
....
....
....
....
....
....
....
....
....

Wishing for things to be well

IS AN EMPTY GESTURE, WITHOUT AN

ACCEPTANCE

OF HOW THINGS ACTUALLY ARE.

Giving thanks every day

WEDNESDAY 7th FEBRUARY

Giving thanks every day

THURSDAY 8th FEBRUARY

....

....

....

....

....

....

....

....

....

....

....

....

....

Gratitude grows naturally

IN THE SPACIOUS FIELD OF

PRESENT-MOMENT AWARENESS.

Giving thanks every day

FRIDAY 9th FEBRUARY

....

....

....

NEW MOON IN AQUARIUS

NH 11.02.24 SH 10.02.24

Aquarius is the sign of the radical, freedom-loving individual and visionary forerunners with whom the rest of society eventually catch up. So why is it that these cool, zany individuals spend so much of their time thinking about their social groups and have a strong impulse to build community and bring people together? The Aquarian Sun highlights the need for acceptance of others as they truly are. Harmony and social cohesion cannot be achieved through control mechanisms, no matter how sophisticated. True social harmony comes about by understanding that every individual is unique and has a specific role to play. No one is excluded. The Aquarian Moon can detach from her feelings and she is quick to assess the qualities of all she meets. Being of unusual character herself, she is able to accept and appreciate the quirks and eccentricities of those she encounters. This New Moon is influenced by one of Aquarius's rulers, Uranus, who is currently in Taurus. Uranus is forming a hard and precise square, meaning that there is some stubbornness in the mix. Is it that ideas take longer to manifest in the material world than we would like? Perhaps the plan needs a tweak. Be open to ideas from curious sources. This New Moon invites us to align with the big ideas and leading thoughts that guide us through life. We are also supported in the social realm – with community building and genuine, real life social networks. Also with friendships and relationships based on shared ideas and ideals, working together to create positive change to our inner personal circle and in the world at large. It is time to align with a universal perspective.

NEW MOON
Intentions

SATURDAY 10th FEBRUARY

....

....

....

....

....

....

....

What have you made peace with?

What still needs to be accepted?

AQUARIUS

MIND

....

....

....

....

BODY

....

....

....

....

SPIRIT

....

....

....

....

SOUL

....

....

....

....

Commitments, Alignments & the Big Letting Go ...

Recently I was sitting in a funky café at Moffat Beach with six girlfriends enjoying a 'Girls Weekend' away. We had rented a beach house and surrendered to the joy of just being with each other. Around the table at the cafe, we shared stories from the heart.

Lou told us that she was disappointed with a long-standing friendship with a girlfriend. Over the last few months, they had arranged to meet up on a number of occasions, yet each time her friend cancelled at the last moment. After the third time this happened, Lou began to feel quite sad.

Lou explained: "I felt like she wasn't giving our friendship any priority at all."

Lou added that she found herself at a crossroads. Should she just let go of the friendship OR should she confront her friend and share her disappointment... Let her know her feelings?

COMMITMENTS

Commitments are an interesting dynamic. Some are made from a deep soul space of love, desire and longing – for example, the commitments made inside a marriage or to bring a child into the world. Others are made from the energy of 'Should' – I should catch up with my parents or friends, or I should visit my grandmother...

What is happening when someone makes a commitment at point A, and then at point B no longer feels like fulfilling that commitment – for whatever reason? It might be that you no longer want to keep the commitment. There might be business pressures, or tiredness factors, obligations with kids, or sickness...

Should we hold to our commitments under all circumstances or is it okay to UN-commit?

What are the consequences if we do not show up for an appointment or to a commitment we have made?

What are the consequences to the relationship?

What are the consequences to ourselves?

What are the consequences, more importantly, to our own soul?

THE ORDER OF LOVE

Firstly, we should think about this issue in relation to the order of love, which is:

1. Love of God
2. Love of Self
3. Love of Others.

If we act OUT OF ORDER, in other words if we put the love – or needs – of others in front of our love of self, this can show up as what I call an OVERRIDE. This is when we feel the need to override our natural soul's inclination in order to please or maintain a commitment to another.

If I make myself go for coffee with a friend, or have that tennis game with my cousins, I have to override any need I might have for rest and space at that moment. I am not honouring my LOVE OF SELF and when this happens, I create damage to my own soul. If I continue to put others before myself, I will unconsciously corrode my SOVEREIGN energy and damage my energetic boundaries. I may also develop a 'martyr' complex if I live in a perpetual state of pleasing others. This does not sound like fun!

WHAT IS THE LOVING ACTION?

1.   HONOUR YOUR FREE WILL IN EACH MOMENT.
     This may look like cancelling or rescheduling. It is always good practice to
     give an honest explanation and to be authentic with your feelings. Our true
     soul friendships will not fall apart just because we are unable to honour all our
     arrangements.

2.   SAY NO TO COMMITMENTS IN THE FIRST PLACE.
     We all have an inner instinct about commitments or invitations that we would
     rather not make or accept. It is amazing how difficult saying 'No' can be for
     some people. Mothers and pet owners need to start this practice early on in
     the piece. If you have difficulty saying no, you might be unconsciously avoiding
     confrontation.

3.   MEET YOUR OWN NEEDS.
     There may be a reason your soul needs to UN-COMMIT. Perhaps your deeper
     spiritual self is knocking quietly on the door of your heart, and you may have
     been barely hearing her. Perhaps you even need to make a life review and
     explore ALL your relationships. Your time is a GIFT, so use it wisely and with
     discernment for the greater good of all.

BEING ON THE RECEIVING END
OF BROKEN COMMITMENTS

Getting back to the café, there was obviously a huge range of triggers that were activated in Lou's soul, in response to a broken arrangement.

Triggers like:

>   I have invested more in this friendship than my friend has
>   I am unimportant and not valued
>   I feel abandoned...

Witnessing this from an objective point of view, it was clear that Lou was embodying inner childhood emotions. With a little prompting and enquiry, the detangling process began.

Here are some good questions to ask yourself next time you feel activated by a change of plan:

1. When have I felt like this before?
2. What memories are my current sadness/anger connected to?
3. Am I avoiding a truth?
4. What is the deeper emotion under what I am feeling?

ALIGNMENTS

Have you ever felt like the universe was not in flow with an idea you have had or an intention?

If appointments have been missed, events cancelled and plans derailed – perhaps it is an alignment issue? If something is not divinely flowing or lining up, the universe is not supporting the decision or connection. At least, not at this moment. There might be SOMETHING ELSE OF GREATER IMPORTANCE needing your attention.

It could also be an indication that 'the Law of Attraction' in the relationship is diminishing. On a soul level, perhaps the relationship is no longer of high value. If too much effort from both parties is needed to keep the relationship on track, the Law of Attraction is changing.

A good example of this is when one party experiences a shift in emotional capacity and awareness, however the other party does not. Lou had been through many initiations in the past 12 months; she was moving more definitely toward her own soul's path. Her frequency had shifted, and this was making it harder and harder for her girlfriend to keep up with her energetically. Being swamped and overwhelmed with her own issues, her friend did not have the capacity for the relationship anymore.

HERE ARE SOME JOURNALING SPACES
TO EXPLORE YOUR OWN ALIGNMENTS.

Have you felt let down or disappointed by a friend? (In relation to appointment changes or broken commitments)

....

....

....

....

....

Has someone broken a commitment to you recently?
What was the situation?

....

....

....

....

....

....

....

What emotions were activated regarding this situation for you?

....

....

....

....

Can you remember a time or place in your childhood when you also felt these same emotions? When you felt let down?

....

....

....

....

....

....

....

....

....

Can you give thanks to this situation now for showing you these dormant emotions?

....

....

....

....

....

....

....

....

....

Can you see a good reason to continue the relationship with the person?
Or would it be a better decision/reason to let it go?

....
....
....
....
....
....

Have you got everything that you need from this relationship already?
(Are you just continuing it out of habit or misguided loyalty?)

....
....
....
....
....

It might be time to look at the relationship – Is it serving you or is it no longer serving you?

....
....
....
....
....
....

Giving thanks every day

MONDAY 12th FEBRUARY

Giving thanks every day

TUESDAY 13th FEBRUARY

....
....
....
....
....
....
....
....
....
....
....
....
....

Commitment

IS WHAT TRANSFORMS A

PROMISE INTO REALITY.

ABRAHAM LINCOLN

Giving thanks every day

WEDNESDAY 14th FEBRUARY

Giving thanks every day

THURSDAY 15th FEBRUARY

....
....
....
....
....
....
....
....
....
....
....
....

As we express our gratitude,

WE MUST NEVER FORGET THAT THE HIGHEST
APPRECIATION IS NOT TO UTTER WORDS

BUT TO LIVE BY THEM.

JOHN F. KENNEDY

Giving thanks every day

FRIDAY 16th FEBRUARY

Giving thanks every day

SATURDAY 17th FEBRUARY

....
....
....
....
....
....
....
....

SUNDAY 18th FEBRUARY

....
....
....
....
....
....
....
....

Giving thanks every day

MONDAY 19th FEBRUARY

Giving thanks every day

TUESDAY 20th FEBRUARY

....
....
....
....
....
....
....
....
....
....
....
....

Let us be grateful to the people who make us happy;
they are the charming gardeners
who make our souls blossom.

MARCEL PROUST

Giving thanks every day

WEDNESDAY 21st FEBRUARY

Giving thanks every day

THURSDAY 22nd FEBRUARY

Commitment is the bridge that connects two souls, allowing them to traverse the journey of life together.

Giving thanks every day

FRIDAY 23rd FEBRUARY

Giving thanks every day

FULL MOON IN VIRGO

How are your intentions coming to fruition?

....

....

....

....

....

....

....

....

....

....

....

....

....

....

....

....

....

....

....

....

....

NH SH 24.02.24

Giving thanks every day

MONDAY 26th FEBRUARY

Giving thanks every day

TUESDAY 27th FEBRUARY

Love is an endless act of forgiveness.

FORGIVENESS IS THE FINAL FORM OF LOVE.

REINHOLD NIEBUHR

Giving thanks every day

WEDNESDAY 28th FEBRUARY

Giving thanks every day
THURSDAY 29th FEBRUARY

Commitment is an act, not a word.

JEAN-PAUL SARTRE

March

S	M	T	W	T	F	S
31	26	27	28	29	1	2
3	4	5	6	7	8	9
10	11	12	13	14	15	16
17	18	19	20	21	22	23
24	25	26	27	28	29	30

IMPORTANT THINGS TO DO

PERSONAL GOALS

SEEDING MY DREAMING

BIRTHDAYS

Giving thanks every day

FRIDAY 1st MARCH

....
....
....
....
....
....
....
....
....
....
....
....
....
....
....
....
....
....
....
....
....

Giving thanks every day

SATURDAY 2nd MARCH

....
....
....
....
....
....
....
....

SUNDAY 3rd MARCH

....
....
....
....
....
....
....

Giving thanks every day

MONDAY 4th MARCH

Giving thanks every day

TUESDAY 5th MARCH

Giving thanks every day

WEDNESDAY 6th MARCH

Giving thanks every day

THURSDAY 7th MARCH

....
....
....
....
....
....
....
....
....
....
....
....
....
....

Gratitude is not an action:

RATHER IT IS A QUALITY OR AN ATTITUDE
THAT ENVELOPS US WHEN WE FULLY SURRENDER
OURSELVES TO THE EXISTENCE OF WHAT IS.

Giving thanks every day

FRIDAY 8th MARCH

....

....

....

NEW MOON IN PISCES

NH SH 10.03.24

Pisces is the final sign in the Zodiac Cycle. It is the great ocean where all the tributaries and rivers wash into. When the Sun shines his light through Pisces, we dream into the timeless quality of our destiny. Timelines overlap and it can feel like all things are possible.

The Pisces Moon is sweet and playful. Highly intuitive, she feels her way through the waters sensing the warm and cold currents – she feels everything and is therefore highly empathic. She inspires peals of laughter one minute and tears of deep sorrow the next. Both expressions are utterly felt and genuine. Tonight, Pisces' traditional ruler, Jupiter is sidling up to Uranus in Taurus. Radiating a sense of optimism and the scintillating possibility that whatever we intend may manifest.

However, in the midst of this emotion we are asked to find the delicate midpoint. This New Moon is situated between Saturn, who counsels common sense and reminds us of consequence. Also, Neptune (the modern ruler of Pisces) who lulls us with sweet song into the most fantastical of dreams and tells us EVERYTHING is possible.

Interesting! To connect with this New Moon, consider what makes your heart sing and what or whom truly aligns you with your soul purpose. Also, would you call yourself a realist or a fantasist? Do you need more of one and less of the other? This is a magical,

NEW MOON
Intentions

SUNDAY 10th MARCH

....
....
....
....
....
....
....
....

Dreams do come true. What is still true for you?

Notice...

PISCES

MIND

....
....
....
....
....
....

BODY

....
....
....
....
....
....

SPIRIT

....
....
....
....
....

SOUL

....
....
....
....
....

Sustainable Salmon ... Really?

Since moving to Tasmania in 2015, my interest in food production has magnified tenfold. The presence of Tasmanian farming practices just cannot be ignored because Tasmania IS a farm! Fruit, wines, cheeses, beef, lamb, goat, poppies, hemp and most obviously, fish!

HOWEVER – LET'S TALK ABOUT SALMON...

The first time I drove past a salmon farm down in the Huon Valley, I was excited by the accessibility I had to these outlets. I pulled into the warehouse expecting to purchase some bargain-priced wholesale fish direct from the factory – what could be fresher than that?! I had been told that salmon is loaded with omega-3 fatty acids, which can assist in optimal cellular function, nervous system regulation, and inflammatory responses. My intent for the winter was to eat as much fresh salmon as possible, so you can imagine how disappointed I was to learn that there was no factory-to-consumer outlet. Nor was there a reception of any kind. The factory appeared 'closed' to the public.

Driving away I became curious about the relationship Tassie fisheries have with local Tasmanians. I unwittingly opened a can of worms when I began asking more questions...

CAGED FISH

I am a little embarrassed to admit that I did not fully comprehend WHERE Australian Salmon came from. I knew it was from 'Down South', because the water is colder here, however I did not understand that there is no such thing as 'wild-caught salmon' in our local waters. Australian Salmon is farmed – ALL of it. Furthermore, as I researched how this farming practice happened, I began to conjure up images of chickens in cages with nowhere to roam – because this is exactly the way our fish are treated.

I can go on and on about the pitfalls of farmed fish... Including; the quality and sustainability of the fish feed, the truckloads of antibiotics fed to the salmon when they are sick, the overstocking and therefore cramped conditions of their environment, the fish shit that pollutes the water way, the death of at least a dozen species of animals including penguins, dolphins, seals, and other protected aqua life. Instead, I am going to recommend you read Richard Flanagan's book, 'Toxic: The Rotting Underbelly of the Tasmanian Salmon Industry'.

Richard is a thorough researcher, yet more importantly, was a local to Bruny Island. Richard used to sit and write his masterpieces while watching the dolphins breach and frolic. However, since the salmon farms were introduced in these waterways he now laments that the D'Entrecasteaux Channel is green with algal bloom. Plus there is not a dolphin in sight! So, Richard's story is personal and firsthand.

Suffice to say, I have not eaten a caged chicken or egg in over 25 years, and I now refuse to eat farmed salmon for exactly the same reasons. The industry does not care.

NOISE

Ocean noise pollution has been recognised for decades as a threat to marine life. Whales and dolphins rely on sound for everything! Communication, foraging, navigation, mating and parental bonding – to name a few. I am sad to learn in my research that marine animals (seals in particular as they love salmon) are pummelled with underwater cannons in order to chase them away. Another noise offender is the growing heavy-industrial noise from boats and giant factory ships. These are some of the biggest commercial boats operating in Tasmania, including the largest well-boat in the world. Their frequency is low and loud as they thud their way up and down narrow, shallow inshore waterways.

Have you ever lain awake trying to screen out the base noise of a 'doof' party?
It is the same for our fish!

At the time of writing this article, no science has been commissioned by either the State Government or the Tasmanian Salmon industry to examine the effects of salmon farming's use of explosives or noise on the whale, dolphin or other marine populations.

I should also give the locals a mention here too – for they are subjected to the barrages of noise, day and night. In addition, they endure flood lights shining into bedrooms!

WHAT ABOUT HEALTH?

Most (if not all) of the studies done on the benefits of eating salmon refer to WILD CAUGHT SALMON. That is: salmon caught in natural environments such as oceans, rivers and lakes. However, half of the salmon sold worldwide comes from fish farms. Farmed fish are fed on high-fat, high-protein diets. In the beginning it was krill and deep-water crustaceans. Although when the supplies of these ran low, fish farmers began using crushed-up chicken meal, which includes the offal, skeletons and feathers.

The latest fish food is now partially soy-based, which has its own story to tell – a story that includes rainforest destruction. When I felt into the idea of my salmon being fed on chicken or soy... Well, it just does not sit right in my stomach, and neither does the salmon.

Fish farming is driving overfishing, with an estimated 25 percent of fish caught globally being used for aquaculture. In other words, caught fish is used to feed caged fish. What is also of concern is the way fishmeal and fish oil is preserved. Unless stabilised with chemicals, fishmeal and fish oil go rancid, losing their beneficial omega-3 oils – the source of salmon's health food status.

The chemical stabiliser of choice is ethoxyquin, which was developed by Monsanto as a pesticide. It is manufactured from petrochemicals, with a range of uses, which include the prevention of rubber cracking in car tyres!! Ethoxyquin ensures fishmeal will not self-combust in transport. This 'benefit' led to the International Maritime Organisation stipulating it as an obligatory fishmeal stabiliser to prevent fires and explosions occurring during transportation and storage.

Sadly, ethoxyquin has been shown to cross the blood-brain barrier of animals and accumulates in the fatty tissue of humans. This can lead to chromosome breakage and is detectable in human breast milk. You guessed it – the major source of ethoxyquin contamination in humans would appear to be aquaculture.

FAT FISH

The diet fed to farmed fish makes these fish super fatty – however not with the kinds of fats we want. The two main polyunsaturated fats are omega-3 and omega-6 fatty acids. These essential fatty acids, or EFAs, play important roles in our body and WE NEED THEM in our diet. However, too many omega-6s could cause increased inflammation and may play a role in heart disease. Farmed salmon contains more fat than wild salmon, and the largest portion of that fat comes from omega-6 fatty acids.

Because antibiotic use in aquaculture is not always controlled, unregulated and irresponsible use of antibiotics has also been a problem in the aquaculture industry. Richard mentioned that only 33 percent of all antibiotics fed to the fish is absorbed, leaving the remaining 67 percent to be excreted back into waterways. With who knows what consequence? Ingesting traces of antibiotics over the long term may cause drug resistance, hypersensitivity to antibiotics, and can disrupt our gut flora.

PINK FISH

I always believed that salmon was fed with beetroot juice in order to create that lovely pink colour. However upon researching, I can not find any reference to this!

Pink Colour and How They Make It

You are who you eat – and what farmed fish eat – which, along with pesticides and antibiotics, according to Quartz.com, is a 'kibble' made from a 'hodgepodge'. This includes the oil and flesh of smaller fish plus corn, gluten, ground-up feathers, soybeans, chicken fat and genetically-engineered yeast. In the wild, salmon feast on crustaceans such as prawns, algae and plankton that are naturally pink in pigment.

Enter 'astaxanthin'. A synthetic variation of this pigment is fed to our salmon to recreate the pink colour of the flesh. Fish farms try to use just the right amount to make fish look palatable. One fish-feed company even offers a sort of colour wheel that shows how the amount of the chemical will affect the colour of salmon.

Astaxanthin can be found in many species such as: lobsters, salmon, shrimps, crabs, as well as birds, like flamingos. It is a lipophilic terpenoid that accumulates in oils and fat.

Today, SYNTHETIC astaxanthin is used for aquaculture and most of the molecules are produced from petroleum sources. Farmed salmon naturally have a light or even grey flesh. To recreate the appealing pink colour, commercial formulations are used. This has been a problem, as many companies do not properly label their product to indicate that a synthetic pigment is used to give the food the 'fresh' colour.

The industry has dyed its salmon for one reason only – to make its product look like wild fish that consumers would buy. Industry research conducted by a group of Norwegian academics shows that when offered the choice, consumers associate quality with colour and are willing to pay more for richer shades of pink.

SEAFOOD FRAUD!

WHAT TO DO?

The fastest way to balance and wholeness is always through AWARENESS. This is why I wrote this article. I remember protesting about a highway being constructed in in my Local Northern Rivers suburb, Ocean Shores, back in the early 1990s. Despite HUGE community effort, the highway went ahead and its noise impacts now disturb many residents. I felt powerless at the time, as it appeared that those in power had ultimate control and were not particularly interested in local opinion. However, moving forward, this fish farming issue is different. YOU HAVE POWER over what you chose to ingest. You are SOVEREIGN over your own body. So if the food you are eating is UNSUSTAINABLE in all ways – destroys ecosystems, damages mating and migration patterns of our whale wisdom keepers, pollutes drinking water, and toxifies your body. YOU do have a choice to CHOOSE LOVE and not to eat it!

Share this information with your family and friends at the next gathering or dinner party. Understand the facts, so that you may intelligently discuss the reasons why YOU do not eat farmed salmon. The fewer people who support the industry, the less fish will be farmed. It is as simple as that. Less demand = less supply.

ALSO you can...

- Find out where you can buy wild salmon. All non-tinned salmon sold in Australia is farmed, other than the 100 percent wild sockeye from **The Canadian Way**.
- Tinned salmon sold at the supermarket is wild if it says 'wild or wild caught'.
- Purchase tinned salmon that is in brine as opposed to industrial processed seed oils high in omega-6's.

Join **NWTAS for Clean Oceans** – because The North West coast of Tasmania is in the firing line for the EXPANSION of Fish Farms.

Connect with **Tasmanian Alliance for Marine Protection (TAMP)**. A Tasmania wide-alliance of groups, which are actively challenging the salmon farming industry and the Tasmanian Government to provide better regulation.

The Tasmanian Department of Natural Resources and Environment Tasmania is a good source of information as they submit plans to the government about commercial fisheries and best practice including salmon plans.

FISH ON LAND?

There is a school of thought that the warming of the oceans will eventually drive salmon farming on to land where the temperature can be controlled. Land-based farming will burn more fuel than open pens, but at least there is no exposure to the ocean, other than fast-flowing, temperature-controlled water, which is pumped in and out of the fish tanks around the clock.

Although land-based fish farming does not solve all the problems faced by the industry, it does remove the issues around fish escapees, sea lice, worms, the pollution of our waterways and homes, and the threats to precious sea mammals and other island dwellers.

My advice, if you want to eat fish, catch it yourself!

Giving thanks every day

MONDAY 11th MARCH

Giving thanks every day

TUESDAY 12th MARCH

....
....
....
....
....
....
....
....
....
....
....

THE UNCHECKED DISCHARGE OF INDUSTRIAL
WASTE INTO OUR WATERS IS A BETRAYAL
OF OUR RESPONSIBILITY TO PROTECT
AND PRESERVE THE EARTH.

JACQUES-YVES COUSTEAU

Giving thanks every day

WEDNESDAY 13th MARCH

Giving thanks every day

THURSDAY 14th MARCH

....

....

....

....

....

....

....

....

....

....

....

WHEN INDUSTRIES *pollute our waterways,*
THEY NOT ONLY HARM THE ENVIRONMENT BUT
ALSO JEOPARDIZE THE HEALTH AND WELL-BEING

OF FUTURE GENERATIONS.

JOHN F. KENNEDY

Giving thanks every day

FRIDAY 15th MARCH

Giving thanks every day

SATURDAY 16th MARCH

....

....

....

....

....

....

....

SUNDAY 17th MARCH

....

....

....

....

....

....

....

Giving thanks every day

MONDAY 18th MARCH

Giving thanks every day

TUESDAY 19th MARCH

....
....
....
....
....
....
....
....
....
....
....

INDUSTRY WITHOUT CONSCIENCE
is a sure-fire recipe for polluting our precious water resources.

MAHATMA GANDHI

Giving thanks every day

WEDNESDAY 20th MARCH

Giving thanks every day

....

....

....

....

....

....

....

....

....

....

....

....

....

Gratitude

HELPS US TO REMEMBER THE GOOD:

A MEMORY THAT IS OFTEN STOLEN BY OUR RESENTMENT.

KERRY HOWELLS

Giving thanks every day

FRIDAY 22nd MARCH

....

....

....

....

....

....

....

....

....

....

....

....

....

....

....

....

....

Giving thanks every day

SATURDAY 23rd MARCH

....
....
....
....
....
....
....
....

SUNDAY 24th MARCH

....
....
....
....
....
....
....

Giving thanks every day

MONDAY 25th MARCH
FULL MOON IN LIBRA – A PENUMBRAL LUNA ECLIPSE

How are your intentions coming to fruition?

Giving thanks every day

TUESDAY 26th MARCH

Giving thanks every day

WEDNESDAY 27th MARCH

Giving thanks every day

THURSDAY 28th MARCH

....
....
....
....
....
....
....
....
....
....
....
....
....

Silent gratitude isn't very much to anyone.

GERTRUDE STEIN

Giving thanks every day

FRIDAY 29th MARCH

Giving thanks every day

SATURDAY 30th MARCH

....

....

....

....

....

....

....

....

SUNDAY 31st MARCH

....

....

....

....

....

....

....

....

April

S	M	T	W	T	F	S
31	1	2	3	4	5	6
7	8	9	10	11	12	13
14	15	16	17	18	19	20
21	22	23	24	25	26	27
28	29	30	1	2	3	4

IMPORTANT THINGS TO DO

PERSONAL GOALS

SEEDING MY DREAMING

BIRTHDAYS

Giving thanks every day

MONDAY 1st APRIL

....
....
....
....
....
....
....
....
....
....
....
....
....
....
....
....
....
....
....
....

Giving thanks every day
TUESDAY 2nd APRIL

....
....
....
....
....
....
....
....
....
....
....

We feel calmer when we express our gratitude because a niggling voice inside has been listened to.

KERRY HOWELLS

Giving thanks every day

WEDNESDAY 3rd APRIL

....

....

....

....

....

....

....

....

....

....

....

....

....

....

Giving thanks every day

THURSDAY 4th APRIL

....

....

....

....

....

....

....

....

....

....

....

....

Gratitude

IS THE FAIREST BLOSSOM
WHICH SPRINGS FROM THE SOUL.

HENRY WARD BEECHER

Giving thanks every day

FRIDAY 5th APRIL

Giving thanks every day

SATURDAY 6th APRIL

....
....
....
....
....
....
....
....

SUNDAY 7th APRIL

....
....
....
....
....
....
....
....

Giving thanks every day

MONDAY 8th APRIL

Giving thanks every day
TUESDAY 9th APRIL

....

....

....

NEW MOON IN ARIES – A TOTAL SOLAR ECLIPSE

NH 08.04.24 SH 09.04.24

Tonight's New Moon is also an Eclipse. Eclipse energy is unpredictable and often disruptive. So instead of placing your intentions into this chaos, we invite you to journal your observations. A type of portal opens between eclipses and this doorway yawned open on the last Full Moon. How have things been these last two weeks? Have you found it erratic and chaotic? Tonight, we are witness to a powerful Solar Eclipse that will be visible in Mexico, America and Canada – the only one to stretch right across the Americas this century. Solar Eclipses occur when the Moon blocks the light of the Sun and the dark side of the Moon lights up. It is like we are out of the conversation, thrown back for a moment, on our own devices without the radiant guidance of the Sun. As it occurs in Aries, themes around our individuality and vital forces come to the forefront. This is especially heightened as the Eclipse occurs on the same degree as Chiron. What lessons are you being shown? Chiron always offers a key, a way through suffering – a guiding thought, experience or encounter that shows you a previously obscured path forwards. Themes around feeling safe being and expressing yourself come up. Can you speak your truth or do you self censure out of fear of being ostracised? How is your life force and vital energy? If you are feeling a little threadbare and exhausted, how might you support yourself?

The Eclipse Portal that has been open for the last two weeks gradually closes.
Who or what has entered your life in this period? Who or what has left?

NEW MOON
Intentions

TUESDAY 9th APRIL

....

....

....

....

....

....

....

Can you speak your truth or do you self-censure
out of fear of being ostracised?

If you're feeling exhausted,
how might you support yourself?

ARIES
♈

MIND

....

....

....

BODY

....

....

....

SPIRIT

....

....

....

SOUL

....

....

....

....

The Healing Power of Psychedelics

BY ALLIE ACKLAND-PRPIC

When Melanie approached me to write an article – I was thrilled. I knew of her work and the beautifully compiled Gratitude Diary – full of love and heart. The power of gratitude is amazing! As a psychologist, I created and ran a program that introduced gratitude diaries into school classes for eight years. It was such a gift to watch these young people light up when they focused on what they are thankful for.

Melanie asked me to write an article about Psychedelics – my other passion. Psychedelics have helped me so much in navigating my personal and professional life. They have informed me about many truths I had not seen, shifted my emotions, given me new insights into, and healed many of my relationships and helped me to be a more present and loving mother. Thank you for the opportunity to share this valuable information Melanie. xoxo

MENTAL HEALTH CRISIS

The rates of depression and anxiety in Western countries today are alarmingly high. In Australia, over 2.2 million people out of a population of 26 million have been diagnosed with mental health conditions, including anxiety and depression. Despite this alarming statistic, there is something new (or not so new?) on the horizon in the way of treatment options: Psychedelics, which are currently going through what people are calling a renaissance!

Psychedelics are powerful psychoactive substances that alter perception and mood, and affect numerous cognitive processes. They are generally considered physiologically safe and do not lead to dependence or addiction.

THE MODERN HISTORY OF PSYCHEDELICS

It is claimed that the 'hippies' of the 1960s and 1970s were birthed from their use of psychedelics, influenced by pioneers such as Albert Hoffman, Ram Dass (Richard Alpert), and Timothy Leary. The Beatles admitted, and then denied, their song 'Lucy (L) in the Sky (S) with Diamonds (D)' was actually about LSD.

These pioneers perceived that the ban on psychedelics was based on the establishment's theory that the increasing use of psychedelics was leading to a rise in 'awareness' – making people less susceptible to the agendas that served those in power. This rise in awareness came to clash with the Nixon Administration in the United States (US) and resulted in a 'war on drugs', when citizens, for the first time in history, refused to go to war, and protested for 'Peace, Love and No War'.

After decades of bans by governments around the world, psychedelics re-emerged in the mental health research sphere around the late 1990s. Since about 2009 the number of research studies into their therapeutic use has been rapidly increasing. The results are looking good, creating renewed hope for successful treatment of mental health conditions.

WHAT'S HAPPENING IN AUSTRALIA

As of July 2023, approved psychiatrists have been able to prescribe and oversee the administration of psilocybin for Depression, and MDMA (entactogen) for Post Traumatic Stress Disorder. This was made possible by the Therapeutic Drugs Administration (TGA) rescheduling these psychedelics for these specific mental health conditions.

Part of the reason MDMA and psilocybin were approved in Australia for these specific mental health conditions, was that the TGA received over 12,000 public submissions in rebuttal of their initial decision to not reschedule them for therapeutic use. This was the largest response the TGA has ever received for any drug being rescheduled. The TGA sat up and paid attention, then later swung their non-approval in the other direction.

CURRENT LEGAL PSYCHEDELIC USE OVERSEAS

In the US, many states have been progressively decriminalising psychedelics including psilocybin, iboga, ayahuasca, San Pedro cactus (mescaline), or entheogens in general. At the time of writing this, psilocybin and MDMA are being lined up for state-wide approval for therapeutic use through the clinical trial pipeline of the Federal Drug Administration (FDA).

In Canada in 2022, it became legal for prescribing Health Care Practitioners to access restricted drugs, including psilocybin, from overseas through a Special Access Program. The Western world is catching onto these substances that many cultures have used for thousands of years, often in ceremonies, to induce altered states and bring about healing.

CURRENT TRENDS

Thanks to best-selling authors such as Michael Pollan whose book, 'How to Change Your Mind', (which was turned into a Netflix series), many people have been asking, 'Is this for me?' and 'Where can I do this?' A wave of people are travelling to countries where they are legal, becoming involved in psychedelic trials, or accessing underground therapy. Yet, with the capacity for people to now access psychedelics legally for therapeutic or personal use in their own country, a new phase of how we can psychologically help people is now being born.

POSITIVE EFFECTS

So, what are the positive results of these mysterious psychedelics? Psychedelics such as psilocybin can help us to integrate ourselves in new ways by disrupting rigid and repetitive thinking, thus creating an opportunity to direct or affect our healing. They can help us to see things from a different, and sometimes, higher perspective. Psychedelics expert, psychologist and neuroscientist, Dr Robin Carhart-Harris says psychedelics offer us an 'unconstrained and hyper-associative mode of cognition'.

Studies show, and vast amounts of people also report, beneficial outcomes from taking psychedelics. These include improved mood, creative stimulation, increased empathy, compassion for self, profound insights into their own life or the world around them, improved relationships and greater wellbeing. Such positive long-lasting effects can be achieved from just 2-3 dose sessions, paired with psychotherapeutic preparation and integration sessions in the days, weeks and months afterwards.

WHAT IS PSYCHEDELIC INTEGRATION?

This is a term you should expect to hear more about in relation to psychedelics. The integration sessions support participants to process their experience of psychedelics in a healthy way – to draw the gold from it, and get the most out of the altered state experience over the long-term. Integration is really about giving yourself the time and space to digest, assess, consider, reflect and process your experience so that your life improves from it in a meaningful way.

RISKS

Like anything, psychedelics do not come without their risks and there are some contraindications, including heart conditions, certain medications, and a personal history of psychosis. Lack of preparation, poor mindsets, unsuitable environments, and recreational use of these drugs can lead to situations where people are negatively affected by their psychedelic experience, especially if they opt out of integration or therapy support.

Having healthy intentions about what you aim to achieve from your psychedelic experience is also important. Taking Psychedelics on a night on the town with friends could lead to a difficult time and it is not recommended to use them without the support of a well-trained psychedelic facilitator. It is important that contraindications are checked, dosage is managed, the environment and personal mindset are good, and integration therapy afterwards is of a good quality. Nonetheless, with preparation, the right mindset, a safe therapeutic setting, and follow-up integration, they can be profoundly healing and revolutionary.

QUESTIONING WHERE WE ARE AT

Today we want to enjoy all the benefits and technology of our 'evolved' world – although the escalating mental health conditions inform us that we are not doing as well as we could be. Not that long ago, our ancestors were much more connected and interconnected to each other and the earth; this was the time when we relied on plants, fire, and water for survival. Could our mental health crisis be a direct result of the present system we have created, serving us on so many levels, yet not our overall wellbeing?

PSYCHEDELICS CAN TEACH US

Global warming and pollution are a reflection of our ways of living – choosing technology and money over the earth's needs. Perhaps therapeutic altered states can teach us something new about how to be, and give us insights into our own decisions and traumas so that we can awaken, refreshed, revived and with greater wellbeing.

HOPES FOR OUR FUTURE

What would a world look like if mental health was improving and national happiness was exploding? A joy-filled planet, free of repression and full of life? How can psychedelics help to improve our wellbeing in ways that we have not managed to achieve with all our advanced technologies? What does a future look like where two sessions with a psychedelic and 10 therapy sessions every two years are the new mode for improved wellbeing – rather than a daily dose of an antidepressant?

We are not so far away from a world where a psychedelic therapy centre is in every suburb with ethical therapists who are well educated in terms of preparation and integration. The hope for humanity is high not only for those with mental health issues, but also for mentally well people who wish to improve other areas of their lives as well.

If you are intending to use psychedelics to improve your wellbeing and have been advised they could help you, with good therapy and integration support, you may be surprised at how healing they can be.

PERSONAL NOTE

Personally, I would really love to see all the cultures of the world move into states of higher belonging, self love, acceptance and forgiveness. I hope that psychedelics can support a transition to a way of being where we embrace each other and the earth more, heal more, cause less harm – understanding the truth of our own power and sovereignty. Psychedelics is an interesting field because it informs us of both the truth and the shadows. Power and financial games will play out, yet at the same time, they will be seen for what they are. There will be little hiding. The time of an evolved society, where wellbeing is valued over profits is hopefully upon us, with psychedelics to assist on the way.

x Allie

Allie Ackland-Prpic is a psychologist and supports people with Psychedelic Integration. Allie has released a Psychedelic Integration Journal available at www.integratepsychedelics.com.au or www.healingpsychology.com.au

Giving thanks every day

WEDNESDAY 10th APRIL

Giving thanks every day

THURSDAY 11th APRIL

....
....
....
....
....
....
....
....
....
....
....
....

LSD, *used wisely and with caution,*

COULD BE FOR PSYCHIATRY WHAT THE MICROSCOPE IS
FOR BIOLOGY OR THE TELESCOPE IS FOR ASTRONOMY.

ALBERT HOFMANN

Giving thanks every day

FRIDAY 12th APRIL

Giving thanks every day

SATURDAY 13th APRIL

....
....
....
....
....
....
....
....

SUNDAY 14th APRIL

....
....
....
....
....
....
....
....

Giving thanks every day

MONDAY 15th APRIL

Giving thanks every day

TUESDAY 16th APRIL

....
....
....
....
....
....
....
....
....
....
....
....

The real journey is an inward one,

EXPLORING THE DEPTHS
OF YOUR OWN CONSCIOUSNESS AND

DISCOVERING YOUR TRUE NATURE.

RAM DASS

Giving thanks every day

WEDNESDAY 17th APRIL

Giving thanks every day

THURSDAY 18th APRIL

....

....

....

....

....

....

....

....

....

....

....

....

*The most important trip you will ever take
is the journey within yourself.*

RAM DASS

Giving thanks every day

FRIDAY 19th APRIL

....

....

....

....

....

....

....

....

....

....

....

....

....

....

....

....

....

Giving thanks every day

SATURDAY 20th APRIL

....

....

....

....

....

....

....

....

SUNDAY 21st APRIL

....

....

....

....

....

....

....

Giving thanks every day

MONDAY 22nd APRIL

Giving thanks every day

TUESDAY 23rd APRIL

....
....
....
....
....
....
....
....
....
....
....
....

PSYCHEDELIC EXPERIENCE

IS ONLY A GLIMPSE OF GENUINE MYSTICAL INSIGHT,
BUT A GLIMPSE, WHICH CAN BE MATURED AND DEEP-
ENED BY THE VARIOUS WAYS OF MEDITATION IN WHICH
DRUGS ARE NO LONGER NECESSARY OR USEFUL.

TIMOTHY LEARY

Giving thanks every day

WEDNESDAY 24th APRIL

FULL MOON IN LIBRA

Have you experienced any eclipse-related ripples these last few weeks?
What themes have you noticed?

....

....

....

....

....

....

....

....

....

....

....

....

....

....

....

....

....

....

NH 23.04.24 SH 24.04.24

Giving thanks every day

THURSDAY 25th APRIL

Giving thanks every day

....
....
....
....
....
....
....
....
....
....
....
....
....
....
....
....
....
....
....

Giving thanks every day

SATURDAY 27th APRIL

....
....
....
....
....
....
....
....

SUNDAY 28th APRIL

....
....
....
....
....
....

Giving thanks every day

MONDAY 29th APRIL

Giving thanks every day

TUESDAY 30th APRIL

....
....
....
....
....
....
....
....
....
....
....
....

In the end, it's not about altering your consciousness;

IT'S ABOUT EXPANDING YOUR CONSCIOUSNESS.

RAM DASS

May

S	M	T	W	T	F	S
28	29	30	1	2	3	4
5	6	7	8	9	10	11
12	13	14	15	16	17	18
19	20	21	22	23	24	25
26	27	28	29	30	31	

IMPORTANT THINGS TO DO

....
....
....
....
....
....
....
....

PERSONAL GOALS

....
....
....
....

SEEDING MY DREAMING

....
....
....
....

BIRTHDAYS

....
....
....

Giving thanks every day

WEDNESDAY 1st MAY

....
....
....
....
....
....
....
....
....
....
....
....
....
....
....
....
....
....
....
....

Giving thanks every day

THURSDAY 2nd MAY

When we make Gratitude a devotional practice,
we honour life
– all of it, the pleasant and the unpleasant –
by offering our full Presence to what is here.

Giving thanks every day

FRIDAY 3rd MAY

Giving thanks every day

SATURDAY 4th MAY

....

....

....

....

....

....

....

....

SUNDAY 5th MAY

....

....

....

....

....

....

....

Giving thanks every day

MONDAY 6th MAY

Giving thanks every day

TUESDAY 7th MAY

....
....
....
....
....
....
....
....
....
....
....
....
....

ALLOW LIFE TO BE.

Giving thanks every day

....

....

....

NEW MOON IN TAURUS

NH 07.05.24 SH 08.05.24

The sign of Taurus celebrates the abundance of the World.
It is not only about having what you need to scrape by, it is about living well
and being surrounded by quality and beauty.

The Taurean Moon is wise, earthy and fertile. She is ready to multiply your intentions,
as generous as a tree laden with fruit. Her gentle and imaginative manner
inspires mothers, artisans, builders and business people alike.

The planetary ruler of Taurus, Venus, is in attendance – auspiciously whispering
her blessings as the Sun and Moon meet in the depths of the velvety sky.
Uranus and Jupiter are also in Taurus. Uranus is loosening long held assumptions
and blockages and, this may feel a little uncomfortable. If you are feeling discomfort
with the changes, welcome in Jupiter's energy. He is beaming forth his infallible
optimism and obliterating fixed thinking and old ideas with his wisdom.

To align your intentions with the flow of tonight's Full Moon, contemplate your
material needs, in a heart-centered way. What do you need, to not just survive
– but thrive? What is needed to help you feel grounded, embodied and secure?
How might you not only attract the beauty and harmony you crave into your life,
but also spread outwards into the world around you?

NEW MOON
Intentions

WEDNESDAY 8th MAY

....

....

....

....

....

....

Survive or thrive?
What is still needed to help you feel secure?

Time to spread your beauty
outwards into the world!

TAURUS

MIND

....
....
....
....
....

BODY

....
....
....
....
....

SPIRIT

....
....
....
....
....

SOUL

....
....
....
....
....

Giving thanks every day

THURSDAY 9th MAY

Resting Chiron

(THE WOUNDED HEALER)

At the time of writing this article I have a huge deadline to meet and it's creating stress in my system. More than ever before ... Ahhh!

BUT Perhaps, I could reframe this moment as a creative portal? Intense, granted... but productive and fruitful. Remembering that what I do often involves awakenings for me and then for others too. I love writing for my readers, exploring what's relevant and what's important. Of late, the theme of the 'Chronic Healer' has emerged for both me and many of my clients. Welcome Chiron – otherwise known as the Wounded Healer.

WHO OR WHAT IS CHIRON?

Well, firstly, Chiron is a small planet in the outer solar system – and since Chiron takes approximately 49 years to circle the Sun whilst journeying through all 12 zodiac signs, we each will go through a 'Chiron return' around the time of our 50th birthday.

This is the time of an 'awakening portal' when our core wounds rear up for another opportunity to be transformed and healed. In fact, everything we've resisted in the past can emerge in this period of time for deeper self-examination. The Chiron return process takes around four years, lingering in the final zodiac sign on its 49th cycle before entering the first zodiac sign under which you were born. If we understand the core wounds we were born with, it is thought that under Chiron's influence we can help our own healing – paradoxically by helping others to heal themselves.

ANCIENT MYTHS

It's hard to say where legends actually come from... Stories are written originating in the stars; and planets are given human personas. Mythical and ancient legends may help us better understand the Chiron archetype.

Chiron was born as a centaur (half man/half horse) as the result of a liaison between the nymph, Philyra, and the god Kronus/Saturn. Philyra was so horrified by Chiron's appearance that she abandoned him. Consequently, Chiron felt unloved and alienated from his people.

The legend says that this beautiful horse/man spent his life healing others and acting as an advisor and teacher to other Greek heroes, including Hercules and Achilles.

Chiron was doomed to live eternally with the pain of his abandonment and isolation. He was also in physical pain from a wound received by a poisoned arrow sent by a drunken Hercules.

Luckily, Chiron held the belief that in life PAIN is the very BEST teacher. He learnt that ACCEPTANCE of what is, is to let suffering go. His wound was in fact his gift.

ASTROLOGY

The great Cosmic myths reveal the story of the battles between Uranus and Saturn. Uranus – the big Daddy, the unpredictable genius with his hot flashes of inspiration interspersed with healthy rebellion. Saturn, more feminine in Nature, represents our earthly physical boundaries of time and structure. Chiron embodies the combination of both the masculine and feminine and is therefore a bridge, a key or doorway between the two. He also reminds us our wounds stem from the soul.

Healing comes naturally when knowing we are ALL ONE in this wounding. In many ways, Chiron has come to set our ego-self free. He awakens us from I AM, to WE ARE.

HOW CHIRON CAN HELP YOU

Chiron is often prominent in a horoscope when feelings of abandonment dominate the psyche. This is usually played out with, or triggered by a parent, a sibling, a partner, a lover, a friend or significant other. Behaviours such as neglect, avoidance or even simple indifference can activate these wounds.

Chiron's legacy is that IF we can become aware of the CORE WOUND we were born with, we can transform and ignite our own healing, primarily by assisting others to heal themselves.

This core wound theme cropped up repeatedly when I was between 48 and 51 years old – my Chiron return. Shame was the prevalent emotion wanting to emerge, however, It took me until almost the end of this passage to realise this as a FELT emotion. Instead, I was often confused, bemused and governed by my Law of Attraction in the game of life. Essentially, I was caught in a loop of recreating the uncomfortable family legacy – the negative feeling that 'everyone I love must die'. It was a wound that began WAY before me, because it had also been a theme for both of my parents. Their stories had become part of my movie. And as the Chiron return grew near, It had cycled back in this time portal to be finally healed and resolved.

FAMILY SECRETS

Sometimes there is a secret or an uncomfortable legacy that is held within our family system. When the truth is suppressed, it's not REALLY hidden because the emotions of the event or circumstance will naturally surface over time throughout the family dynamic. It is only when we can connect to the 'origin of the wound' that we can understand the emotional and mental weight we have been carrying, whether conscious or unconscious, on behalf of our beloved family members.

During your own Chiron return, stories and weird scenarios may emerge from your dream space, and leap from the unconscious to the conscious.

MENTORS

Because the nature of the Chiron wound is often rooted in abandonment and aloneness, having or being a mentor can result in life-changing relationships for Chironic people.

In the myth, Chiron was not alone for long. His quick mind and positive attitude impressed the Sun god, Apollo, who adopted Chiron as his own. He was able to complete his apprenticeships in the arts of healing, medicine, poetry, prophecy and logic. Chiron's love for knowledge was a warm blanket for his lonely heart. Because of his accumulated knowledge, Chiron had a 'destiny urge' to lead, heal and assume responsibility for the transformation of pain on this planet. The paradox here is that his strong drive to learn and better himself came from the motivation of his PAIN.

Those operating under a strong Chironic influence may be dissatisfied with the hand they were dealt at birth and feel compelled to want to heal others and the planet. Their true karmic return, however, is to take rest in the deeper truth, that all is well – as it currently is – and that the healing of the world and the planet does not rest on their shoulders alone.

NATURE

Apart from his vast intellect and hunger for knowledge, it is said that Chiron had an innate connection to the earth – after all, he was half horse. He was able to discover the healing qualities in nature. All other centaurs honoured him as their leader, for he had wisdom and a reserve that was unique to him.

Chiron connects the wound of separation with the innate connectedness in ALL things. Chiron was able to embody the divine quality of WISDOM and to go on to share this wisdom as his gift to humanity. It was the gift of evolutionary human development and transformation. The gift of alchemy: from lead into gold, from pain into freedom...

BACK TO MY DEADLINE!

Yesterday I had a mentoring session with someone whose spiritual wisdom I value. I invited my Gratitude Diary team to the meeting as we were discussing the future of the Diary and my role in it. The session was phenomenal, and afterwards, I took a debrief with my friend and confidant, Ariel, who is also an astrologer. Ariel suggested that we, as a team, meet once a month for the sole purpose of supporting one another on our journey.

I became excited by the prospect, and immediately shifted to: 'Yes, and this can be a course that we can offer the world – Healing the Chronic Healer'.

Ariel, who knows me well, said: 'Yes, but take a step back... I'm suggesting we just do this for ourselves, for each other'.

And I said again: 'YES, BUT we can do A, B and C too...'

And on it went. It was only on the third attempt to get me into a receptive state that I realised what Ariel was calling out to me to STOP doing.

She was offering an invitation for me to end my relentless desire to be a Healer and to finally do something just for MYSELF. I've been SO driven to assist others, to play my role and pay any dues I thought I owed, that I was on autopilot. Any opportunity that was just for my own healing, was somehow overlooked and deemed not important.

I'm resting now, in the sweet surrender that I too am coming to the end of my own Chironic Healer Journey... resting in the truth that I matter. I always did. It was never my fault. I'm worthy of God's love. As we all are!

Looking at which sign Chiron was transiting through at the time of your birth, can help guide you to make sense of your own wounds throughout this lifetime.

Chiron through the Signs

EXPLORING THE WOUND AND ACTIVATING HEALING

ARIES

The Wound – Issues of self-worth and self-identity. Deep-seated self-doubt makes it difficult for you to speak your truth, causing you to go it alone and conceal emotions. This can create the compensatory behaviours of arrogance, hard-headed stubbornness, and a rebel-without-a-cause mentality.

Healing Comes When – You accept and love yourself as you are. Taking pride in your independence and strength doesn't mean that you have to go it alone.

TAURUS

The Wound – Issues of neglect and lack. Early experiences of; hunger, emotional neglect, lack of spiritual guidance, and being bullied for being poor can create the compensatory actions of overspending, addictive tendencies, and being overly materialistic. Holding a grudge could be holding you back as well.

Healing Comes When – You know that you are love and that it is an inexhaustible resource. Open your heart and share the love – it will come flowing back threefold.

GEMINI

The Wound – Issues around communication and relating to others. Difficulty in expressing your ideas, and crippling shyness. Misinterpreting information and social cues, and being a subject of gossip and sharp tongues. This can create the compensatory actions of either becoming a recluse or talking over the top of people for fear you will not be heard or understood – possibly bending the truth as well in order to be accepted.

Healing Comes When – You trust that you are connected to divine truth, and you realise that you are a skilled thinker and communicator. Words are powerful beyond measure; they have the capacity to either harm or heal. You have a special gift to unfold.

CANCER

The Wound – Issues of dissociation and feeling like you don't belong. Believing yourself to be unlovable, due to complications of childhood trauma connected to family life and feelings of being ostracised. This can create the compensatory actions of clinging onto people and situations that don't return your love or favour.

Healing Comes When – You realise that you are deserving of the same maternal and loving care that you show others. Nurture, love and respect yourself and the loving energy that you crave will stream towards you.

LEO

The Wound – Issues of feeling left out and that your hidden talents will never be recognised after having your self-worth and creativity thwarted at a young age. This can create compensatory tantrum-throwing and bullying to get attention and your own way in order to be seen and heard.

Healing Comes When – You connect to your creative and unique individuality. When you let go of external reward-seeking behaviours and step into creating for the love of the thing itself, then your charisma will shine out and naturally attract accolades and the respect of those around you.

VIRGO

The Wound – Issues of seeking perfection at the expense of personal relationships and love. Getting lost in the details and forgetting the 'why' can leave you feeling unloved and like a servant, rather than as a valued member of your community. This can create the compensatory actions of complaining, nit-picking and being overly critical of everyone around you and how they do, or don't do things.

Healing Comes When – You can step back from the minutia and survey the whole landscape – and take time to enjoy it! Realise that the world is going to keep running even if you stop, and that you are loved simply for being you, and not just for what you can do for others.

LIBRA

The Wound – Issues of interpersonal wounding. Breakdown of relationships and the inability to find closure. Fear of being rejected from the group and a crippling doubt that you will ever find a peaceful and loving relationship. This can create a compensatory lean towards co-dependency – suffocating friends, family and partners, thus driving them further from you.

Healing Comes When – You realise that the fear of losing others is greater than the reality of being on your own. When you find the capacity to stand alone and be fulfilled as an individual, you will attract healthy partnerships.

SCORPIO

The Wound – Issues of loss and deep grief. This could be a loss of innocence, trust, or faith. This can create the compensatory actions of pushing people away, wounding them before they hurt you. Also getting involved in manipulative mind games and trying to control outcomes so as to avoid further wounding, sometimes ending in self harm.

Healing Comes When – When you realise that you're always transforming, nothing is permanent. Apply your intuitive, emotional and sensitive nature to your spiritual path. Focus less on controlling others; soon they will be approaching you with their deepest stories for guidance.

SAGITTARIUS

The Wound – Failure to launch, feeling that you are destined for greatness, but never catching the lucky break needed. Being in the wrong place at the wrong time. Abuse around fanatical, ideologically-driven people – be it cults, relatives or others. This can create compensatory behaviours of self-importance and aggrandisement. Swinging between ideologues in the hopes of salvation.

Healing Comes When – When you connect to the wisdom inherent in yourself and live through principles close to your heart, others will seek you out for the natural teacher and role model that you are.

CAPRICORN

The Wound – Issues of workaholicism, overly pragmatic thinking, being overly materialistic, and blindly ambitious can drive you into deep melancholy and despair. This can create compensatory moods of nihilism, cynicism and bitterness that drive people away from you.

Healing Comes When – You place your skill, commitment and sense of responsibility in the service of love itself. Allow it to unfold within you. The more you protect and serve the innocent, the greater the love and respect you'll have for yourself.

AQUARIUS

The Wound – Issues of identity, of appeasing groups with ideas and behaviours so as not to be rejected and outcast. You might harbour a belief that no one is ever going to understand the real you, leading to feelings of crippling isolation and loneliness. This can lead to a self-harming rebellious nature that pre-empts getting ostracised for actions that are harmful to the social order.

Healing Comes When – You be yourself. You were born to individuate and lead by example, not to be a follower. When you become the fully present version of yourself, you allow others to see that they too can have the courage to unfold themselves.

PISCES

The Wound – Issues of childhood difficulties associated with irresponsible adults, which may be through ungrounded spiritualism, addictive tendencies or mental illness. Loss, abandonment, neglect and a general dissociated feeling can turn you into an escape artist – alcohol, food, video games, gambling and bouts of fantasy. The difficulty in staying grounded and connected thwarts your ability to fulfil your destiny.

Healing Comes When – You own your destiny; step out of victimhood and realise that you are the hero of your life's story. Recover your faith that the 'Great All That Is' has a plan for you and that you haven't, for even an instant, been forgotten or unloved.

Chiron the wounded... HEALER IN MY LIFE
BY PATRICIA DARLING

I am sharing my story in the hope that it will inspire and assist others to find peace in their lives.

MY BIRTH STORY

I was given away shortly after birth. Under the title of 'father' on my birth certificate it states 'unknown'. I felt 'different' in my early years – not the same as my friends who had 'normal parents'. I spent a lot of time in my life seeking love as a way of getting some sort of weird confirmation of myself. I exchanged surnames with some of my partners hoping that would propel me into my rightful place on earth. These partners were emotionally broken themselves – and were often less focussed than I was. Trying to heal my 'damaged partners' became my life mission. My signature.

FINDING MY FAMILY

When I was 32, after my biggest life blessing of having my own beautiful daughters, I finally found my birth mother and siblings via DNA and Ancestry searches. I'd always dreamed of a reunion happening – I'd expected to fit right in just like a missing piece of a puzzle. But, it didn't happen like that for me... I was, however, given a name for my birth father, and eventually tracked this man down. We had a great connection and then BOOM – DNA tests showed No Match! We 'adopted' one another anyway, but sadly, Brian, the lovely, kind man who so much wanted to be my Dad, passed away.

MY CHIRON RETURN

I suffered from the core wound of 'Abandonment' most of my life. The wound was very deep, and I may not have survived it, had it not been for the lessons I learnt during Chiron's return in my Astrological birth chart. I developed an interest in finding more about the archetypical 'wounded healer', whom legend has it was born as a centaur (half man/half horse). I learnt that just as Chiron was abandoned by his mother, Philyra, and father, Saturn, before being adopted by Apollo, I was also given up at birth and brought up by a loving, adoptive parent. I was also born with my sun sign in Leo.

Developing an understanding of Chiron assisted me to connect with my core wound of separation. The influence of my Chiron return drove my behaviours, choices and the very essence of my life. I became a caring, healing, empath, putting others needs before my own – just like the Chiron archetype. Whilst this was not an ideal way to exist in the world, it was the 'something' that gave me PURPOSE.

I helped other children, damaged and rejected by the system, find their place in society. I also helped heal women, who had suffered abuse, to regain their self-esteem and confidence, and to learn to make choices to support and care for themselves.

CHIRON'S GIFTS

Chiron showed me that my intuitive healing guidance for others came from the pain I had suffered myself. My lessons became my teachings, and therefore my strengths. How I owned my trauma became the pathway of learning, healing and releasing my own core shadow wound. We humans have free will of course, but sometimes we need to repeat a toxic pattern until our soul learns it is a lesson.

Eventually I found the place for myself where I enjoy being ME. I also made some clear decisions and one was that I was never going to live with a partner again – 'I didn't need anybody'. However, there was one man who also had made some clear decisions – he wasn't going to give up on me! He loves me unconditionally and trusted me to find my true self. We have now been together for nine years, and married for six. In my life today, I also now have four grandchildren who have extended my own tribe, and broken the pattern of abandonment that has shrouded my maternal line. I am loved. I am worthy.

It is very humbling to be part of something as huge as the universe. Now I know I always was. All the animals I rescued, insects set free, birds I whistled back to, and trees I hugged, all heard my soul whispers. The truth is, I was never actually separate. It just took the first half of my life to understand this.

Giving thanks every day

FRIDAY 10th MAY

Giving thanks every day

SATURDAY 11th MAY

....
....
....
....
....
....
....
....

SUNDAY 12th MAY

....
....
....
....
....
....
....
....

Giving thanks every day

MONDAY 13th MAY

Giving thanks every day

TUESDAY 14th MAY

Chiron's energy encourages us to embrace our wounds and use them as catalysts for growth and transformation.

DONNA CUNNINGHAM

Giving thanks every day

WEDNESDAY 15th MAY

Giving thanks every day

THURSDAY 16th MAY

....
....
....
....
....
....
....
....
....
....
....
....

Emotions are like rivers,

THEY CONNECT US TO OTHERS AND REMIND US OF OUR

SHARED HUMANITY.

UNKNOWN

Giving thanks every day

FRIDAY 17th MAY

....

....

....

....

....

....

....

....

....

....

....

....

....

....

....

....

....

....

....

Giving thanks every day

SATURDAY 18th MAY

....
....
....
....
....
....
....
....

SUNDAY 19th MAY

....
....
....
....
....
....
....

Giving thanks every day

MONDAY 20th MAY

Giving thanks every day

TUESDAY 21st MAY

....

....

....

....

....

....

....

....

....

....

....

The best way to find yourself
is to lose yourself in the service of others.

MAHATMA GANDHI

Giving thanks every day

WEDNESDAY 22nd MAY

Giving thanks every day

THURSDAY 23rd MAY
FULL MOON IN SAGITTARIUS

How are your intentions coming to fruition?

Giving thanks every day

FRIDAY 24th MAY

Giving thanks every day

SATURDAY 25th MAY

....
....
....
....
....
....
....
....

SUNDAY 26th MAY

....
....
....
....
....
....
....

Giving thanks every day

MONDAY 27th MAY

Giving thanks every day

TUESDAY 28th MAY

....

....

....

....

....

....

....

....

....

....

....

....

The purpose of human life is to serve and to show compassion and the will to help others.

ALBERT SCHWEITZER

Giving thanks every day

WEDNESDAY 29th MAY

Giving thanks every day

THURSDAY 30th MAY

....

....

....

....

....

....

....

....

....

....

....

NO ONE IS USELESS IN THIS WORLD
WHO LIGHTENS THE BURDENS OF ANOTHER.

CHARLES DICKENS

Giving thanks every day

FRIDAY 31st MAY

....
....
....
....
....
....
....
....
....
....
....
....
....
....
....
....
....
....
....
....

IMPORTANT THINGS TO DO

....
....
....
....
....
....
....

PERSONAL GOALS

....
....
....
....

SEEDING MY DREAMING

....
....
....
....

BIRTHDAYS

....
....
....

June

S	M	T	W	T	F	S
30	27	28	29	30	31	1
2	3	4	5	6	7	8
9	10	11	12	13	14	15
16	17	18	19	20	21	22
23	24	25	26	27	28	29

Giving thanks every day

SATURDAY 1st JUNE

....
....
....
....
....
....
....
....
....

SUNDAY 2nd JUNE

....
....
....
....
....
....
....
....

Giving thanks every day

MONDAY 3rd JUNE

Giving thanks every day

TUESDAY 4th JUNE

....
....
....
....
....
....
....
....
....
....
....
....

Gratitude

IS THE PEACEFUL BRIDGE BETWEEN

THE PAST AND THE PRESENT.

RUMI

Giving thanks every day

WEDNESDAY 5th JUNE

Giving thanks every day

THURSDAY 6th JUNE

....

....

....

....

NEW MOON IN GEMINI

NH SH 06.06.24

The Gemini Sun lightens up our thinking and ideas move with greater ease and mobility.
The Gemini Moon is quicksilver fast, her feelings dance like glimmers of light on the surface
of a lake – ideas flicker and are felt, then discarded or stored for future reference.
She, of all Moons, knows that changing her mind is her perogative.

Mercury (Gemini's ruling planet), Venus and Jupiter are also in Gemini at the moment.
With Mercury at home, communication is free flowing and open,
with a touch of humour and frivolity.

Venus, at the precise degree of the New Moon, supports us lovingly. She lends her grace
and light-hearted touch to beautify our minds and to remind us of how elegant we can be.

Jupiter is sidled together with Mercury and conversations may become so interesting
that they amble on for hours. Jupiter expands all he touches and brings a sense
of optimism and enthusiasm. Wisdom is flowing! Be open to receiving it – maybe through
that long conversation or possibly from a book, a podcast or from deep within,
through meditation and contemplation.

Tonight is a wonderful opportunity to create intentions themed around communications
of all type. Who would you love to share your ideas with? Do you have a project that you are
planning that needs a little extra focus? Would study help you get where you need to go?

NEW MOON
Intentions

THURSDAY 6th JUNE

....

....

....

....

....

....

....

*What are you still holding back on
that still needs to be communicated?*

GEMINI

MIND

....

....

....

....

BODY

....

....

....

....

SPIRIT

....

....

....

....

SOUL

....

....

....

....

To Be or Not to Be

I remember when I was engaged to be married and it was time to choose a ring. My partner and I looked at many different ring designs with gemstones, but I just didn't feel a heart connection with any of them. I didn't resonate with the diamonds and rubies, or any of the other stones I was shown. The rings were also very expensive, which made me feel conflicted. So much societal conditioning around spending up big on a wedding ring as a measure of love and commitment!

Around the same time, I watched a movie called 'Blood Diamond' and realised there is so much loss and bloodshed in the diamond industry. No wonder I was finding it hard to find the right wedding ring – which was supposed to be the symbol of our love! I remember asking myself, why aren't people using pearls to symbolize their love?

Pearls are natural and come directly from the ocean. They are a perfect expression of God's beauty and his kingdom underwater – which is where all life comes from originally. I decided to look more deeply into the energy of the pearl. I did some homework, and oh my goodness, I was just not prepared for what I uncovered when I started researching the pearl.

Pearls are the birthstone for all Gemini and Cancer souls born in June.

Pearls are created in partnership with living creatures. When an oyster, mussel, or clam attempts to soothe the part of its body that has been invaded by a parasite or granule of sand, it does so by creating a soft layered coating over the irritated area, which is known as a nacre. The sea animal will add layer after layer of it until a glistening pearl is formed. This profound process creates pearls in both saltwater and seawater environments.

Pearls arrive perfect as they are. No two pearls are the same and these natural beauties remain one of Earth's most treasured gifts. Pearls come in many different shapes – classic, irregular Baroque, flattened Button, and Keishi freeform pearls. Their colours range from white to gray, with overtones that include; green, gold, brown, purple, bright yellow, pink, silver, blue, or black. My favourites are sometimes infused with a mystical iridescence glow that reflects rainbow tones.

When evaluating pearls, it's not about shape or colour, rather, it's all about the pearl's surface lustre, its brilliance, and how it reflects light. The more brilliant and mirror-like the surface of the pearl, the higher the quality. A dull or chalky surface makes for an inferior pearl.

THE SPIRITUAL MEANING OF PEARLS

In the spiritual traditions of Buddhism, Taoism, and Hinduism, pearls celebrate wisdom and invite awareness of the divine. They have become known through the ages as conduits for relaxation and introspection, and used to alleviate symptoms related to lung diseases including asthma, bronchitis, and tuberculosis. They have also been used to negate the effects of poison, and attract other-worldly protection. It is claimed that they can stimulate the heart chakra, reduce fevers, eradicate allergies, promote the growth of new cells, and help new mothers relax when giving birth.

Apparently, the wisest oysters face the moon when adding their final layers of nacre (inner shell layer) to their creations. This is why the pearl is known to be representative of a powerful feminine energy, a creator of life and worlds.
As energetic magnets, pearls can deepen our connections to our core values. When used in rituals, they can induce loving feelings, positivity, and harmony in all of our relationships. While the Romans saw pearls as representative of high status, the Quran suggests that pearls can be found in paradise.

THE HEALING PROPERTIES OF PEARLS

Pearls can be used to heal our bodies and create balance in our lives – just as gemstones are said to. They can be calming and centering, and can nurture our faith, loyalty, integrity, and purity. No matter our gender, pearls can help us reach equilibrium with a vital, balanced, feminine energy. Perhaps most importantly, pearls embody specific frequencies and energy vibrations that can re-balance deficiencies in the body and spirit.

Throughout history pearls have also been used to treat the digestive tract, muscular systems, and skin.

PEARLS AS A SUPERFOOD?

Pearls are packed with the virus/bacteria killer, glutathione superoxide dismutase (SOD), plus the magnesium in pearls helps our bodies improve our levels of GABA (gamma-aminobutyric acid). Many healers use magnesium to combat depression, anger, unreasonable fears, anxiety, mental obsessions, and insomnia. Pearl powder from capsules can be used in smoothies, salads, and beverages. With its plentiful supply of amino acids, this unique gemstone is a powerful addition to any diet. It is considered safe to consume in small quantities.

THE DIFFERENT TYPES AND PROPERTIES OF PEARLS

Pearls have a long list of healing and metaphysical properties akin to crystals. Each type of pearl has been attributed with different healing properties:

Mother Of Pearl

Heightens intuition, psychic sensitivity, and imagination. Attracts prosperity, protects from negative influences. Protects children.

Pink Pearls

Supports the Sacral and Heart Chakras.

Gold Pearls

Said to promote successful marriages, profitable ventures, divine guidance, and protection. Used in rituals that invite our ancestors to support our relationships and endeavours.

Abalone Pearls

Encourages feelings of love, beauty, gentleness, peacefulness, and joy. Reduces liver heat and symptoms that include headaches, dizziness, spasms of the limbs, and conditions of the eyes.

EARTH'S GIFTS

My research into pearls has me rather in awe. They are considered the only gem born from a consciousness of self-nurturing and the result is just so much beauty. Given the amazing qualities of pearls can you see a reason for choosing them to symbolise a love that's eternal? I can!

What does Sustainability mean to you?

....

....

....

....

....

What changes could you be making within your own home and family for a more sustainable future?

....

....

....

....

....

How can you contribute to a sustainable world? (Dream BIG)

....

....

....

....

....

Giving thanks every day

FRIDAY 7th JUNE

Giving thanks every day

SATURDAY 8th JUNE
WORLD OCEAN DAY

....

....

....

....

....

....

....

....

....

SUNDAY 9th JUNE

....

....

....

....

....

....

....

....

Giving thanks every day

MONDAY 10th JUNE

Giving thanks every day

TUESDAY 11th JUNE

....

....

....

....

....

....

....

....

....

....

....

....

....

The heart of man is very much like the sea,

IT HAS ITS STORMS, IT HAS ITS TIDES AND IN ITS DEPTHS

IT HAS ITS PEARLS TOO.

VINCENT VAN GOGH

Giving thanks every day

WEDNESDAY 12th JUNE

....

....

....

....

....

....

....

....

....

....

....

....

....

....

....

....

....

Giving thanks every day

THURSDAY 13th JUNE

....

....

....

....

....

....

....

....

....

....

....

Water, air, and cleanness
are the chief articles in my pharmacy.

NAPOLEON BONAPARTE

Giving thanks every day

FRIDAY 14th JUNE

....

....

....

....

....

....

....

....

....

....

....

....

....

....

....

....

....

....

....

....

Giving thanks every day

SATURDAY 15th JUNE

....
....
....
....
....
....
....
....

SUNDAY 16th JUNE

....
....
....
....
....
....
....

Giving thanks every day

MONDAY 17th JUNE

Giving thanks every day

TUESDAY 18th JUNE

....
....
....
....
....
....
....
....
....
....
....
....

THE PEARL IS THE QUEEN OF GEMS AND THE GEM OF QUEENS.

GRACE KELLY

Giving thanks every day

WEDNESDAY 19th JUNE

....

....

....

....

....

....

....

....

....

....

....

....

....

....

....

....

....

....

Giving thanks every day

THURSDAY 20th JUNE

Giving thanks every day

FRIDAY 21st JUNE

Giving thanks every day

FULL MOON IN LEO

How are your intentions coming to fruition?

....
....
....
....
....
....
....
....
....
....
....
....
....
....
....
....
....
....
....
....
....
....

NH 21.06.24 SH 22.06.24

Giving thanks every day

MONDAY 24th JUNE

Giving thanks every day

TUESDAY 25th JUNE

....
....
....
....
....
....
....
....
....
....
....
....

*A pearl is a precious jewel
that has been nurtured by nature and time,
emerging as a symbol of purity and grace.*

UNKNOWN

Giving thanks every day

WEDNESDAY 26th JUNE

Giving thanks every day

THURSDAY 27th JUNE

....
....
....
....
....
....
....
....
....
....
....
....

Pearls are the ultimate symbol of

ELEGANCE, SOPHISTICATION, AND TIMELESS BEAUTY.

COCO CHANEL

Giving thanks every day

FRIDAY 28th JUNE

Giving thanks every day

SATURDAY 29th JUNE

....
....
....
....
....
....
....
....

SUNDAY 30th JUNE

....
....
....
....
....
....
....

July

S	M	T	W	T	F	S
30	1	2	3	4	5	6
7	8	9	10	11	12	13
14	15	16		18	19	20
21	22	23	24	25	26	27
28	29	30	31	1	2	3

IMPORTANT THINGS TO DO

....
....
....
....
....
....
....
....

PERSONAL GOALS

....
....
....
....

SEEDING MY DREAMING

....
....
....
....
....

BIRTHDAYS

....
....
....

Giving thanks every day

MONDAY 1st JULY

....
....
....
....
....
....
....
....
....
....
....
....
....
....
....
....
....
....
....

Giving thanks every day

TUESDAY 2nd JULY

....
....
....
....
....
....
....
....
....
....
....
....

WHEN WE ARE IN A STATE OF GRATITUDE FOR ANOTHER,
WE ARE ABLE TO LISTEN MORE ATTENTIVELY TO THEM.

KERRY HOWELLS

Giving thanks every day

WEDNESDAY 3rd JULY

....
....
....
....
....
....
....
....
....
....
....
....
....
....
....
....
....
....
....
....
....
....

Giving thanks every day

THURSDAY 4th JULY

Giving thanks every day

FRIDAY 5th JULY

....

....

....

....

....

....

....

....

....

....

....

....

....

....

....

....

....

....

....

....

Giving thanks every day

....

....

....

NEW MOON IN CANCER

NH 05.07.24 SH 06.07.24

The Sun has been radiating his light through the constellation of Cancer for a few weeks now. He is in the Moon's home, and his guiding beams shine light on our emotional nature. When the Moon is at home in Cancer, she is at her most motherly, nurturing and protective. She exudes emotional understanding, empathy and she nourishes with her understanding, cooking and her capacity to turn even a hovel into a safe and cosy home.

Feelings about how we were nurtured and nourished, memories of sadness and childhood abandonments may arise. This is a time to nurture and love any neglected parts of yourself that emerge.
Integrate them with warmth and love – invite them back home.

Venus, on a journey all of her own, finds herself in Cancer and involved in another New Moon. Here, Venus offers her kindness and beauty to realms of family life and friendship circles. She beautifies everyone. Foolish competitive urges get dropped and it is women supporting women with love and giggles, and possibly cake!
Mars, in earthy Taurus, is playing a supportive, grounding role in the background.

To align with the New Moon in Cancer energies, consider themes relating to family, friends and your emotional life. This a perfect time to reflect on who we consider family. Is there anyone feeling left out who is in need of extra love and attention?

NEW MOON
Intentions

SATURDAY 6th JULY

....
....
....
....
....
....
....

Who is YOUR family?

Who is in need of extra love?

Who feeds your soul?

CANCER

MIND

....
....
....
....
....

BODY

....
....
....
....
....

SPIRIT

....
....
....
....
....

SOUL

....
....
....
....
....

Stairway to Heaven

(22 LAYERS TO THE SPIRIT WORLD)

Do you believe in life after death?

I always have. Of course, I can't prove there is life after death... because I'm not there yet. But, without a doubt, if I had to wager a bet, I would stack all my odds on the affirmative. When it comes to the study of the eternal truths from the mystery schools, there have been those who, over the centuries, have held onto the ancient wisdoms of our world in order to preserve truth. It is said that at the time of the destruction of Atlantis, 12 boats left the city hours before the cataclysm. They journeyed into 12 different directions of the globe and seeded what was to become the 12 tribes; the grandparents of our humanity.

One of these tribesmen was Jesus Christ. When he was born, Jesus had a memory of his Divine Nature, and so he set out to teach his community the pathways to living as a divine human being. Jesus worked closely with his counterpart, Mary Magdalene, and together they studied the mystery schools mentioned above, often travelling to Egypt as part of their mission.

Moving forward 2000 years, I had the pleasure of meeting a very awakened soul, AJ Miller, who has a clear and concise understanding of the Universe and the laws by which it is governed. I've been a seeker most of my life, but never before have I encountered someone who has such a detailed explanation of how the spirit world works.

I studied with AJ Miller for over 10 years, and I continue to be deepened by the clarity of his consciousness and the depth of his love and understanding. From AJ's teachings, I'll share with you some of the knowledge handed down from the ancients.

GOD IS AN ENTITY

But what does this mean? Well, God has feelings. God also has the desire for truth and love to reign supreme for his children – us. I know it's hard to imagine God as someone who has a feeling body, however when I do, something in my own heart softens and becomes receptive to my own Humane-ness. Where did God come from? Well, no one knows the answer to that question. Perhaps this is why these ancient places of spiritual study were called 'Mystery' schools – for the creation of God IS a mystery.

GOD IS MASCULINE/FEMININE IN NATURE

Yep, God is a he/she – both the 'receptive' and the 'penetrating'; neither man nor woman, and with both yin and the yang aspects constantly vibrating in relation to the two aspects of our soul. This he/she revelation should not be too much of a stretch for us to reflect upon – after all, that is how our own souls are in truth. It's only society that has conditioned us into believing we are one gender or the other. We live a very polarised way of life with different dress codes, hairstyles, employment roles, domestic responsibilities and gender restrictions.

God's desire to have children was to express 'his/her' love and these children are US! We were created so that God could express love. That, in and of itself, is something that I am just, OMG, having to ask you to sit with. Because if your receptivity channels are not open to God's love, due to the ways you were conditioned as a child, your receptivity pathway may not have awakened yet.

All Souls are created from love... and in God's image (billions of us), and yes, even those of us who came from unwanted pregnancies or other less than perfect or adverse situations. In essence, we were and are, loved.

THE SPIRIT WORLD

God created many interdimensional spaces, or spheres that are separated by interstellar boundaries – otherwise known as 'Boundaries of Love'. The only way to cross each interstellar space is to progress your awareness and to grow in love.

Perhaps this was God's divine way of creating loving boundaries between souls who are vibrating at different frequencies. This is why our Law of Attraction is working for us in the sphere of our own vibrational state – like attracts like.

TWENTY-TWO STAIRS TO HEAVEN

God the creator, created a six-dimensional universe. God also created the laws that govern this universe. The spirit world is ALWAYS expanding laterally, says AJ, however the spirit world has also expanded vertically, from the seventh dimension upward to the 22nd level of dimensional reality.

Two thousand years ago there were six interdimensional spheres. Since then, 16 more spheres have been created – not by God, yet by God's laws. The first person who entered the 6th sphere, then created the seventh, and so on. Mini gods! Souls such Buddha, Gandhi, and Mother Teresa are known as sixth dimensional beings.

Also created was a descending scale – stairs that went down! These dimensions are of a lower frequency, created from a degradation of love through unloving choices.

Sadly, over time mankind's condition has degraded to such a degree that most souls still reside in the first sphere. Otherwise known as 'lost souls', these entities have suffered trauma, pain and loss. This does not mean these souls are bad, it means they have suffered a degradation of their soul's condition. The bible refers to the first sphere as 'hell'. Billions of people are stuck in this first dimension mainly because they feel separate and will not listen to guidance. Rigid thinking will also keep you stuck here on earth.

LEVEL 22
LEVEL 21
LEVEL 20
LEVEL 19
LEVEL 18
LEVEL 17
LEVEL 16
LEVEL 15
LEVEL 14
LEVEL 13
LEVEL 12
LEVEL 11
LEVEL 10   MANS
LEVEL 9   SPIRITUAL
        EVOLUTION
LEVEL 8
LEVEL 7
LEVEL 6
LEVEL 5   GODS
LEVEL 4   EXPRESSION
LEVEL 3   SOUL LESSONS
LEVEL 2   LEARNED BY
       LIVING
LEVEL 1   3D

WE WERE ALL ANGELS

All children are conceived in a sixth-dimensional state. However, depending on the soul condition of our parents, babies can 'take on' lower emotional frequencies. It is simply what higher dimensional (more loving) children do. It is an unconscious act. However, CARE (at the soul level) can rapidly change their physical state in a positive way, and they can raise their vibrations of love.

All of us, right now, are currently in the sphere we are resonating at in terms of the vibration of love. We do not have to wait until we leave our body in order to progress our soul. We can develop in love while we are here on earth – to move up spheres. Jesus experienced full conscious awareness of the tenth sphere whilst he was in a human body.

MAKING CHOICES THAT ARE HARMONIOUS WITH LOVE

Giving in a way that is congruent with love creates MORE LOVE and the more love created, the better our soul condition will be. Soul PROGRESSION happens when we abide by God's laws that govern the universe.

However, if we continue to make choices that do not come from the seat of love, our soul condition can decline. Our soul-destroying choices include: judging (self and others), lying, manipulating for personal gain, being greedy, exploiting others, indulging in addictive-behaviours, and overriding other's free will. There are SO MANY of God's laws, and we will have a conversation about them another time. But for now, can you feel what might progress your own soul and what might keep you stuck, or even lower your soul condition?

At the end of the day, God gave us free will. We are free to hang out in whatever dimension we choose. We will not be judged. Personally, I would like to continue to progress my own soul and with that intent, I continue to give thanks for the Law of Attraction, for I know it will guide me home.

If you are interested in learning more about the secrets of the Universe, you can find AJ's teachings on YouTube: @Divinetruthmain.

How are your life choices affecting your soul journey?

Choices that progress my soul

Choices that delay my soul's progression

....
....
....
....
....
....
....
....
....
....
....
....
....
....
....
....
....
....

....
....
....
....
....
....
....
....
....
....
....
....
....
....
....
....
....
....

What do I like about myself?

1. ....
2. ....
3. ....
4. ....
5. ....
6. ....
7. ....
8. ....
9. ....
10. ....
11. ....
12. ....
13. ....
14. ....
15. ....
16. ....
17. ....
18. ....
19. ....
20. ....
21. ....
22. ....

Giving thanks every day

MONDAY 8th JULY

Giving thanks every day

TUESDAY 9th JULY

....
....
....
....
....
....
....
....
....
....
....

THE SPIRITUAL WORLD
is the world of eternal truths,
infinite love, and boundless joy.

WILLIAM ELLERY CHANNING

Giving thanks every day

WEDNESDAY 10th JULY

....

....

....

....

....

....

....

....

....

....

....

....

....

....

....

....

Giving thanks every day

THURSDAY 11th JULY

....
....
....
....
....
....
....
....
....
....
....

The spiritual world is not a distant place;

IT IS PRESENT WITHIN US, WAITING TO BE

DISCOVERED AND EMBRACED.

WILLIAM BLAKE

Giving thanks every day

FRIDAY 12th JULY

Giving thanks every day

SATURDAY 13th JULY

....
....
....
....
....
....
....
....

SUNDAY 14th JULY

....
....
....
....
....
....
....

Giving thanks every day

MONDAY 15th JULY

....
....
....
....
....
....
....
....
....
....
....
....
....
....
....
....
....
....

Giving thanks every day

....
....
....
....
....
....
....
....
....
....
....
....

Just as a lake reflects the beauty around it,

OUR EMOTIONS REFLECT THE DEPTHS OF OUR SOUL.

Giving thanks every day

WEDNESDAY 17th JULY

Giving thanks every day

....
....
....
....
....
....
....
....
....
....
....
....

EMOTIONS ARE LIKE PONDS,
*still and tranquil on the surface
but teeming with life beneath.*

Giving thanks every day

FRIDAY 19th JULY

Giving thanks every day

SATURDAY 20th & SUNDAY 21st JULY
FULL MOON IN CAPRICORN

How are your intentions coming to fruition?

....

....

....

....

....

....

....

....

....

....

....

....

....

....

....

....

....

....

NH SH 21.07.24

Giving thanks every day

Giving thanks every day

TUESDAY 23rd JULY

....
....
....
....
....
....
....
....
....
....
....
....
....

Our emotions are like lakes,

HOLDING THE REFLECTIONS OF OUR INNER WORLD.

DIVE IN AND EXPLORE THE DEPTHS

Giving thanks every day

WEDNESDAY 24th JULY

....
....
....
....
....
....
....
....
....
....
....
....
....
....
....
....
....
....
....
....
....
....

Giving thanks every day

....

....

....

....

....

....

....

....

....

....

....

....

We are not human beings having a spiritual experience:
we are spiritual beings having a human experience.

PIERRE TEILHARD DE CHARDIN

Giving thanks every day

FRIDAY 26th JULY

Giving thanks every day

SATURDAY 27th JULY

....
....
....
....
....
....
....
....

SUNDAY 28th JULY

....
....
....
....
....
....
....

Giving thanks every day

MONDAY 29th JULY

Giving thanks every day

TUESDAY 30th JULY

....
....
....
....
....
....
....
....
....
....
....
....

I WOULD MAINTAIN THAT THANKS
ARE THE HIGHEST FORM OF THOUGHT,
and that gratitude is happiness doubled by wonder.

GILBERT K. CHESTER

Giving thanks every day

WEDNESDAY 31st JULY

IMPORTANT THINGS TO DO

PERSONAL GOALS

SEEDING MY DREAMING

BIRTHDAYS

August

S	M	T	W	T	F	S
28	29	30	31	1	2	3
4	5	6	7	8	9	10
11	12	13	14	15	16	17
18	19	20	21	22	23	24
25	26	27	28	29	30	31

Giving thanks every day

....
....
....
....
....
....
....
....
....
....
....
....

*Feelings, like water,
have the power to cleanse and heal,
to wash away the old
and make way for the new.*

Giving thanks every day

FRIDAY 2nd AUGUST

....

....

....

....

NEW MOON IN LEO

NH SH 04.08.24

The Sun is right at home in Leo, radiating from
the centre of our universe directly into our hearts.

In Leo, the Moon finds herself precautious with a knack for high drama. She loves the big feelings, the ones that align with those gorgeous Leonine qualities – honour, dignity and love. She is affectionate and expressive with her love, finding joy in the happiness of those around her. She brings warmth and a playful mood wherever she goes.

Mars and Jupiter are supportive of this New Moon, and they are active over in Gemini. They could be working on a ginormous, inspired project – something with a hundred moving parts or a thousand pages. Or they could be slashing and dismantling fixed and false belief systems and then exploring new and more current ideas and ways to operate.

The North Node always calls us to our future. Tonight it is forming a helpful trine to the New Moon from Aries. Reminding us to hold onto our individuality, to be brave and to take courage as we walk to meet our destiny.

As you make your New Moon intentions, connect with your heart. What and who is it you really love? How do you express and receive love? Do you allow room for creativity

NEW MOON
Intentions

SUNDAY 4th AUGUST

....
....
....
....
....
....
....

Connect with your heart.

What and who is it you really love?

LEO

♌

MIND

....
....
....
....

BODY

....
....
....
....

SPIRIT

....
....
....
....

SOUL

....
....
....
....

Mini Mini Fish Tale

I remember me between the ages of three and five, my family lived in a big older-style home with two giant palm trees in the front yard that were often full of sparrows. In the bathroom, there was a green enamel bathtub, which had a yellow-coloured lion gargoyle as the water spout for the bath.

I recall getting in the bath and being mesmerised with the lion's head. All my cousins were mesmerised by it as well. They'd come around and want me to turn the tap on so we could all watch the water come out the lion's mouth. It was just so mystical and exciting!

Often, while admiring the lion, I'd dunk myself. I'd go deeper under the water until I was completely submerged and then blow bubbles out. I'd lie there, motionless... still... under the water. It was a profound connection for me – being in a beautiful pool of wet, warm with all the noise from the outside world drowned out. I often found outside noise quite intense and not always pleasant.

Every time my aunty came to visit, she would ask, 'Where's Melanie?', and my mother would say, 'In the bath'. I'd be in the bath for the whole time she visited – sometimes for up to three hours. Hence, I inherited the nickname, Mini Mini Fishtail. It was a song on the radio at the time. I remember Aunty Jan saying, 'You're not a little girl, I'm sure you're a mermaid'. And so it stuck – I was called 'Minnie fish' for short.

When I was old enough to go to the swimming pool, I'd do the same. I'd dunk myself under the water while everyone else was diving off the boards, showing off, playing, and throwing balls. I would explore what was happening UNDERNEATH. I'd swim around looking at people's legs, admiring and studying the way they were moving in slow motion. I'd swim towards bubbles, and laugh at how air would get caught under people's shorts. I'd stay under for as long as I possibly could.

The endless summer days at the pool would further cement that feeling of my connection with water, of being more comfortable under the surface than on land – the feeling, I guess, of being a half land and a half sea creature. The feeling of, well... being a mermaid. Consequently, I've always had a strong affinity with the archetype of the mermaid.

We are not separate:
Her and I
Her and you
We share the same ecosystem.

MERM-OLOGY

My inner mermaid loves water. For me, being under or in water is an opportunity to REVITALISE and to transcend any negative thoughts or emotions I feel burdened with.

WATER is vital for life and growth and is often associated with birth and rebirth. I guess this is why mermaids are often depicted as being forever youthful and beautiful – the eternal merry maid. She is said to have the wisdom to shapeshift any earthly problem by becoming one with the ocean.

Mermaids are said to have the rare gift of hydro-kinesis, which is the ability to manipulate water. They have been accused of luring sailors to their death with their magical singing voices – not to mention their bare breasts! As ships approached craggy rocks, beckoned by her song, storms are said to have been conjured up, causing shipwrecks and drownings.

The negativity of this story did not feel right for me – for how could such a divine and happy creature have such resentment and murderous rage.

Then, the lights went on...

These ships... leaking oil. Capturing too many fish. Vibrating harsh noise frequencies in the ocean's depths. Disrupting the ocean's delicate ecosystem that supports life itself...

The mermaid is a custodian
She has a purpose
She is the wisdom of the water and knows all its secrets
She is queen of her realm
The sovereign custodian
Living between two worlds
Sea and earth
Between life and death
She is called a siren
For she will sound hers whenever necessary to bring us to account
It was never sexual
It was an alarm
For all creatures
We have gone too far

MER-MYTH

Mermaid has just so much mythology, legend, folktale and folklore around her. Clearly she has been with us for a very, very long time.

If you are interested in the folklore of mermaids I suggest you do some research. I found some fascinating information at mermaidsofearth.com/on-the-origin-of-mermaids/ .

There are such diverse and amazing stories from all around the world, mermaids pictured in cave paintings dating back thousands of years ago, and mythical tales passed from so many different cultures of the world. Tales of magical and prophetic powers, music and song...

Living between the worlds
Sea and earth
Life and death
Existing in liminal space

PROFESSIONAL MERMAIDS

I grew up with dolls – baby dolls and then Barbie dolls. However, for many of the little girls born in the 1990s and beyond, they've been playing with toy mermaids. The mermaid industry is now worth billions. You can buy mermaid tails, go to a mermaid show, take mermaid swimming lessons and be photographed as a mermaid. You can purchase mermaid accessories – crowns and tiaras, tops made of shells, and just about anything else you can imagine that is associated with being a mermaid.

In recent decades mermaids have also taken on more and more of the role as ambassadors for ocean preservation, ocean conservation and the prevention of marine pollution, overfishing and anything else that contributes to endangering marine species.

SHE'S BACK

Isn't it interesting that mermaids have remerged into our culture. Is it because our oceans are suffering and desperately need a voice? What's her message to you?

Giving thanks every day

MONDAY 5th AUGUST

Giving thanks every day

TUESDAY 6th AUGUST

....
....
....
....
....
....
....
....
....
....
....
....

Thousands have lived without love,

NOT ONE WITHOUT WATER.

W.H. AUDEN

Giving thanks every day

WEDNESDAY 7th AUGUST

Giving thanks every day

THURSDAY 8th AUGUST

....
....
....
....
....
....
....
....
....
....
....
....
....

WATER IS THE DRIVING FORCE OF ALL NATURE.

LEONARDO DA VINCI

Giving thanks every day

FRIDAY 9th AUGUST

Giving thanks every day

SATURDAY 10th AUGUST

SUNDAY 11th AUGUST

Giving thanks every day

MONDAY 12th AUGUST

Giving thanks every day

TUESDAY 13th AUGUST

We never know the worth of water

TILL THE WELL IS DRY.

THOMAS FULLER

Giving thanks every day

WEDNESDAY 14th AUGUST

Giving thanks every day

THURSDAY 15th AUGUST

....
....
....
....
....
....
....
....
....
....
....
....

The environment
IS WHERE WE ALL MEET;
WHERE ALL HAVE A MUTUAL INTEREST;

IT IS THE ONE THING ALL OF US SHARE.

LADY BIRD JOHNSON

Giving thanks every day

FRIDAY 16th AUGUST

Giving thanks every day

SATURDAY 17th AUGUST

....
....
....
....
....
....
....
....

SUNDAY 18th AUGUST

....
....
....
....
....
....
....

Giving thanks every day

MONDAY 19th AUGUST

Giving thanks every day

TUESDAY 20th AUGUST
FULL MOON IN AQUARIUS

How are your intentions coming to fruition?

....
....
....
....
....
....
....
....
....
....
....
....
....
....
....
....
....
....
....

NH 19.08.24 SH 20.08.24

Giving thanks every day

WEDNESDAY 21st AUGUST

Giving thanks every day

....
....
....
....
....
....
....
....
....
....
....
....

WATER IS THE SOUL OF THE EARTH.

W.H. AUDEN

Giving thanks every day

FRIDAY 23rd AUGUST

....
....
....
....
....
....
....
....
....
....
....
....
....
....
....
....
....
....

Giving thanks every day

SATURDAY 24th AUGUST

....

....

....

....

....

....

....

....

SUNDAY 25th AUGUST

....

....

....

....

....

....

....

....

Giving thanks every day

MONDAY 26th AUGUST

Giving thanks every day

TUESDAY 27th AUGUST

....

....

....

....

....

....

....

....

....

....

....

THE MERMAID

IS AN ARCHETYPAL IMAGE THAT REPRESENTS
A WOMAN WHO IS AT EASE

in the great waters of life.

CLARISSA PINKOLA ESTÉS

Giving thanks every day

WEDNESDAY 28th AUGUST

....

....

....

....

....

....

....

....

....

....

....

....

....

....

....

....

....

....

Giving thanks every day

THURSDAY 29th AUGUST

....
....
....
....
....
....
....
....
....
....
....
....

I must be a mermaid.

I HAVE NO FEAR OF DEPTHS
AND A GREAT FEAR OF SHALLOW LIVING.

ANAIS NIN

Giving thanks every day

FRIDAY 30th AUGUST

Giving thanks every day

SATURDAY 31st AUGUST

....
....
....
....
....
....
....
....
....

SUNDAY 1st SEPTEMBER

....
....
....
....
....
....
....
....

September

S	M	T	W	T	F	S
1	2	3	4	5	6	7
8	9	10	11	12	13	14
15	16	17	18	19	20	21
22	23	24	25	26	27	28
29	30	1	2	3	4	5

IMPORTANT THINGS TO DO

PERSONAL GOALS

SEEDING MY DREAMING

BIRTHDAYS

Giving thanks every day

MONDAY 2nd SEPTEMBER

NEW MOON IN VIRGO

NH 02.09.24 SH 03.09.24

The Sun shines his clarity through the constellation of The Virgin. Highlighting her special qualities and inspiring us to step into roles of service – be it towards those close to us or causes that we feel passionate about.

The Virgo moon has the capacity to work hard – she is diligent and methodical. To her, chaos is just a mess that has not been categorised and sorted through correctly. Her skills at untangling complex knots, be they emotional or practical, are legendary.

In earthy Virgo, Mercury (the planetary ruler) is the master of analysis. Figuring out the correct order in which to tackle any project for maximum results. Currently in Leo, he acts as an enthusiastic ally – encouraging us to face some of the larger life puzzles that are presenting themselves to us at this time.

Saturn in Pisces is situated opposite the New Moon, counselling us to apply the wisdom we have learnt through our lives. Saturn is backing you to set realistic and attainable goals. Yet at the same time Mercury in Leo says: 'Sure, take it seriously, but it doesn't have to be boring! Enjoy the process.'

To align with the New Moon in Virgo's flow, tune your intentions into: How might I be of service and to whom? How am I at organising – Is there a project that is in need of clarity? How is the house – does it need some love and cleaning? How is my health – could I be serving my dear body better?

NEW MOON
Intentions

TUESDAY 3rd SEPTEMBER

....
....
....
....
....
....

How might I be of service and to whom?

VIRGO

♍

MIND

....
....
....
....
....
....

BODY

....
....
....
....
....

SPIRIT

....
....
....
....
....

SOUL

....
....
....
....
....

Salt & Balance

I often ask my friends, what is something that you eat that you couldn't go without? Their answers often include chocolate! Personally, I couldn't live without SALT. I've had quite a healing journey with salt, which is why I decided to write this article.

A LONG HISTORY

When we think of the chemical substances that contribute to the welfare of mankind, we rarely think of sodium chloride – ordinary 'kitchen salt'.

Salt has been used by humans since the beginning of time. It's not just a taste enhancer, it's something our bodies need. It's also the crucial substance that has allowed humans to preserve and store food for long periods of time – think cured meat stored over long winters when conditions were too harsh for hunting.

In ancient times, salt was a highly prized commodity – so much so that during the Roman Empire it was used as currency. The word 'salary' comes from the word 'sal', the Latin word for salt. This is why the expression 'not worth his salt' indicates someone who isn't worth the salary they are paid.

WHY DO WE THROW SALT OVER OUR SHOULDERS?

According to tradition, spilling salt is bad luck. The antidote is to then throw over your shoulder, preferably your left shoulder. By throwing salt over your shoulder, it is believed that the evil spirits associated with spilt salt can be rendered powerless. Even Buddhists have followed the tradition of throwing salt over their shoulder after someone's funeral. This is done to prevent spirits from entering their house.

There is a biblical connection to salt in the Old Testament's story of Lot's wife disobeying God's instructions by turning back to look at Sodom. As punishment he turned her into a pillar of salt. Many believe that this story signifies that the devil is always behind you, so throwing salt over your shoulder is a symbolic way to chase the devil away.

WHY IS BREATHING SALTY AIR GOOD FOR US?

Breathing salty air, which contains negative ions found in natural environments like oceans, can also have positive effects on our health. Negative ions can boost mood, reduce stress, and improve respiratory function.

SALT – THE ESSENTIAL MINERAL

Salt is an essential mineral that plays a vital role in the optimal functioning of the human body. It helps balance water inside and outside our cells, regulates blood pressure, and maintains the balance of positive and negative ions in the body.

As a nurse I often witnessed patients being given an IV line of sodium and water in hospitals. Makes sense as a first base to replenish the lost water and salt in the body caused by medical conditions. The body needs sodium to work properly.

I had a long stint of adrenal fatigue, and its effects have lingered with me a lot of my adult life. I've recently had a healing breakthrough drinking electrolyte hydration drinks, made using a powder which contains sodium with added potassium and magnesium. Thank you to Rob and his team at LMNT for all their great advice. For more information see the LMNT website: drinklmnt.com

HOW MUCH SALT DO WE NEED?

The recommended daily intake of sodium is around 6g, according to the World Health Organisation, but the amount you need is unique to your constitution, age, gender and overall health. The American Heart Association recommends that most adults should only consume 2.3g of sodium per day, which is equivalent to one teaspoon. There is a problem with these metrics though – as the quality of the salt we imbibe is important to consider too.

TABLE SALT

Commercial table salt, the kind you get from Coles and Woolworths, is the stuff most of us grew up eating. It is highly refined and contains additives, including iodine and anti-caking agents. Potassium ferrocyanide, calcium silicate, silicon dioxide, yellow prussiate of soda and iron ammonium citrate.

Personally, I aim to avoid preservatives and additives in my food. I'm also allergic to silicon so most commercial salts are not so safe for me.

Commercial manufacturing of salts strips naturally occurring essential minerals such as calcium, magnesium and potassium from table salt. I've always wondered about why this is done as these minerals are so good for the body. Perhaps it has something to do with the taste profile of commercial salts? Apparently, magnesium is removed because it can have a laxative effect in some individuals. Personally, I'd prefer my salt still had magnesium in it.

Salt which contains essential minerals such as calcium, magnesium, and potassium is crucial for maintaining healthy bones – especially during menopause when estrogen levels decline.

UNREFINED SALTS

Unrefined salts, such as sea salt produced by evaporating seawater, are generally lower in sodium and higher in essential minerals. Sea salt is harvested from seawater and retains trace amounts of minerals like magnesium and calcium. Unrefined salts include: Grey salt, also known as Celtic Sea Salt; Black salt, such as black lava salt and kala namak; Red salt, like Hawaiian red salt; Fleur de sel, a premium finishing salt harvested along the French coastline; Persian Blue salt harvested from an ancient Salt Lake in Iran; and Himalayan salt, sourced from ancient sea beds and ancient salt mines in the Himalayan mountains. This salt is highly regarded for its mineral content and contains all 84 essential trace elements required by the body.

Other types of salt include kosher salt, which is less dense and commonly used in kosher cooking, and rock salt, primarily used for de-icing roads and sidewalks.

TABLE SALT VERSUS UNREFINED SALTS

Unrefined salts are generally healthier choices as they contain lower sodium levels and higher essential mineral content compared to table salt.

Table salt is a highly refined version of salt, which is created by superheating natural salt to 1,200 degrees Fahrenheit – in the process destroying most beneficial compounds. Some medical experts claim that table salt is responsible for many sodium-related health issues, in comparison to unrefined salts which may heal the body instead of harming it.

Compared to table salt, sea salts can be a good unrefined choice, as they contain smaller quantities of natural iodine, higher levels of essential minerals, and lower levels of sodium. However, there is a concern about pollutants, especially microplastics in our ocean coastlines. Microplastics have infiltrated almost everything. It's good to keep yourself informed and to balance your sea salt consumption with other earth-bound salts.

EFFECTS ON THE HEART

High levels of salt can cause your blood pressure to rise, which can increase your risk of heart disease or stroke. By contrast, too little sodium or salt can lead to low blood pressure. My understanding is that by ingesting 'X' amount of salt, the effect of that salt in your body may be directly proportional to the amount of fluid I'm washing it down with.

For instance, the quickest way to elevate low blood pressure is to drink beverages rich in electrically charged minerals called electrolytes. The main electrolytes are sodium, calcium, potassium, chloride and phosphate. The benefits of electrolytes include regulating the body's nerves, muscles, water balance, PH levels, blood pressure, and the repair of damaged tissue.

ADRENAL FATIGUE AND SALT

There is a relationship between adrenal fatigue and salt. Adrenal fatigue, experienced by over 80 per cent of the worldwide population, presents significant health problems including: brain fog, insomnia, low energy, irritability, poor concentration, and difficulty waking up in the morning. It can disrupt the sodium balance in the body and increase the need for sodium intake. People with adrenal fatigue often experience salt cravings.

Himalayan Pink salt, with its trace minerals, has been reported to help reduce adrenal exhaustion by inducing better sleep; restoring sodium content; promoting hormone secretion, especially anti-stress hormones; and aiding in efficient energy conversion. It can also help detox the body if you use Himalayan crystal baths and salt lamps.

DEHYDRATION AND SALT

Dehydration occurs when the body loses water. Symptoms include thirst, dark urine, low urine volume, dry skin, fatigue, muscle cramps, dizziness, constipation, nausea, headache, and irritability. Inadequate fluid intake is a common cause of dehydration, particularly in the elderly who may have unreliable thirst mechanisms.

Dehydration can lead to low blood pressure due to the decrease in blood volume. Low blood pressure is generally undesirable as it hampers the delivery of oxygen and nutrients to tissues. Symptoms of low blood pressure include dizziness, fatigue, lightheadedness, nausea, blurry vision, irregular heartbeat, and, in severe cases, shock.

Chronic dehydration has been linked to high blood pressure, especially in individuals with diabetes and hypertension. To stay hydrated, it is important to consume enough fluids and electrolytes, particularly sodium. Drinking electrolyte water can help prevent dehydration and maintain a normal blood volume. Getting the balance of our water intake can be tricky. Drinking too much water can dilute blood sodium levels and lead to an electrolyte imbalance, exacerbating blood pressure issues.

Be adventurous with salt – have an affair with it! Find out which type of salt works best for you and journey beyond what's in the salt shaker on the table...

Giving thanks every day

WEDNESDAY 4th SEPTEMBER

....

....

....

....

....

....

....

....

....

....

....

....

....

....

....

....

....

....

Giving thanks every day

THURSDAY 5th SEPTEMBER

....
....
....
....
....
....
....
....
....
....
....
....

Salt

IS BORN OF THE PUREST OF PARENTS:

THE SUN AND THE SEA.

PYTHAGORAS

Giving thanks every day

FRIDAY 6th SEPTEMBER

....
....
....
....
....
....
....
....
....
....
....
....
....
....
....
....
....
....
....

Giving thanks every day

SATURDAY 7th SEPTEMBER

SUNDAY 8th SEPTEMBER

Giving thanks every day

MONDAY 9th SEPTEMBER

....

....

....

....

....

....

....

....

....

....

....

....

....

....

....

....

....

....

....

....

Giving thanks every day

TUESDAY 10th SEPTEMBER

....
....
....
....
....
....
....
....
....
....
....
....

Salt is the policeman of taste:

IT KEEPS THE VARIOUS FLAVORS OF A DISH IN ORDER AND
RESTRAINS THE STRONGER FROM TYRANNIZING OVER THE WEAKER.

LUCIEN TENDRET

Giving thanks every day

WEDNESDAY 11th SEPTEMBER

Giving thanks every day

THURSDAY 12th SEPTEMBER

....
....
....
....
....
....
....
....
....
....
....
....

SALT IS BORN OF THE PUREST OF ELEMENTS,
the water and the sun,
AND IT POSSESSES THE POWER
TO HEAL AND RESTORE BALANCE.

PARACELSUS

Giving thanks every day

FRIDAY 13th SEPTEMBER

....
....
....
....
....
....
....
....
....
....
....
....
....
....
....
....
....
....
....
....

Giving thanks every day

SATURDAY 14th SEPTEMBER

....
....
....
....
....
....
....
....

SUNDAY 15th SEPTEMBER

....
....
....
....
....
....
....

Giving thanks every day

Giving thanks every day

....
....
....
....
....
....
....
....
....
....
....
....

Gratitude is more than a feeling:

IT'S AN ACTION.

KERRY HOWELLS

Giving thanks every day

WEDNESDAY 18th SEPTEMBER

FULL MOON IN PISCES

How are your intentions coming to fruition? What has shifted? What has changed?

....
....
....
....
....
....
....
....
....
....
....
....
....
....
....
....
....
....
....
....

Giving thanks every day

THURSDAY 19th SEPTEMBER

....
....
....
....
....
....
....
....
....
....
....
....
....
....
....
....
....
....
....
....
....

Giving thanks every day

FRIDAY 20th SEPTEMBER

Giving thanks every day

SATURDAY 21st SEPTEMBER

....
....
....
....
....
....
....
....

SUNDAY 22nd SEPTEMBER

....
....
....
....
....
....
....

Giving thanks every day

MONDAY 23rd SEPTEMBER

Giving thanks every day

TUESDAY 24th SEPTEMBER

....
....
....
....
....
....
....
....
....
....
....
....

*There is no need to mentally construct
things to be grateful for:
Gratitude is an act of being present
WITH what is.*

Giving thanks every day

WEDNESDAY 25th SEPTEMBER

Giving thanks every day

THURSDAY 26th SEPTEMBER

Giving thanks every day

FRIDAY 27th SEPTEMBER

Giving thanks every day

SATURDAY 28th SEPTEMBER

....
....
....
....
....
....
....
....

SUNDAY 29th SEPTEMBER

....
....
....
....
....
....
....

Giving thanks every day

MONDAY 30th SEPTEMBER

IMPORTANT THINGS TO DO

PERSONAL GOALS

SEEDING MY DREAMING

BIRTHDAYS

October

S	M	T	W	T	F	S
29	30	1	2	3	4	5
6	7	8	9	10	11	12
13	14	15	16	17	18	19
20	21	22	23	24	25	26
27	28	29	30	31	1	2

Giving thanks every day

TUESDAY 1st OCTOBER

....
....
....
....
....
....
....
....
....
....
....
....
....
....
....
....

WE ARE ABLE TO UNDERSTAND *gratitude*
MORE FULLY IF WE SEE IT IN CONTRAST WITH ITS
opposite: RESENTMENT.

KERRY HOWELLS

Giving thanks every day

WEDNESDAY 2nd OCTOBER

....

....

....

NEW MOON IN LIBRA – SOLAR ECLIPSE

NH 02.10.24 SH 03.10.24

The Libran Moon is as sweet as they come; she never wants to upset anyone, let alone be the cause of disharmony. You may have come across her, always getting to the bottom of "who said what" and trying to heal rifts. She is a master at mediation, it is like the air she breathes. Yet, once that is sorted out, you will find her scoping out the latest fashions and beautifying everyone and their cat. The way she changes the mood of a space with artfully-placed flowers can change hearts and minds – for the better.

Venus, Libra's planetary ruler, is in Scorpio. Meaning that feelings and desires, privately and quietly, are running deep. Mercury and the South Node (our past) are bracketing this New Moon, creating nostalgia and giving us much to talk about. Have feelings about a past situation emerged? Or perhaps someone has returned?

Aries sits opposite Libra, counterbalancing social-minded consciousness with the innate needs of the individual. The North node in Aries is tugging at our sleeve. Whose needs are getting steamrolled for the 'good' of the group – Yours? Or are you unwittingly smothering someone with niceness?

As this is a Solar Eclipse New Moon, we suggest not placing intentions, rather observe what messages the Universe is delivering to your doorstep. Look for themes around self and others – the individual and the group for clues. What lessons have you learnt?

NEW MOON
Intentions

THURSDAY 3rd OCTOBER

....

....

....

....

....

....

....

Have feelings about a past situation emerged?

Or perhaps someone has returned?

LIBRA

MIND

....

....

....

....

BODY

....

....

....

....

SPIRIT

....

....

....

....

SOUL

....

....

....

....

The Lost Soul of Atlantis

It is strange how a phrase can become a 'truth' in the minds of the people who use it. Take, for example, the 'Lost City of Atlantis'. Will Atlantis ALWAYS be referred to as 'Lost', if that is what we call it?
I am curious.

Recently, I was interested enough in the city of Atlantis to want to learn more about its relevance in our history. After all, this story is well known as one of the oldest and greatest mysteries of our civilization. What became overwhelming in my research was how many rabbit holes there are, leading in so many different directions, when it comes to the theories of WHERE Atlantis actually was and why it disappeared.

PLATO'S MEMOIRS.

In his memoirs, 'Plato's dialogues', Plato (who was on earth around 400 years before Christ) spoke of the destruction of the ancient and powerful city of Atlantis. As myth has it... its inhabitants had become an ugly and morally-corrupt race. So Zeus and other Gods destroyed the city by sinking it into the ocean, very quickly – supposedly, within 48 hours. Plato believed this took place over 9,000 years before his time.

A Greek myth also tells the story of a great city, which was protected by the Greek God, Poseidon. Who made his son, Atlas, the king of the city – which was then renamed as Atlantis. Makes sense.

In this myth, the city's inhabitants grew more and more powerful, their thirst for power intensified and their ethics declined. It is said that the Atlantean armies ruthlessly conquered the inhabitants of Africa, Egypt, and Europe, as far as Italy. By way of divine punishment, the Gods acted and the island city was beset by earthquakes and floods, and sank into the sea.

WHERE IS ATLANTIS?

Popular opinion and the name Atlantis, would indicate that the city is located in the middle of the Atlantic Ocean, somewhere between America and Africa. However, to this day there has been no evidence found for this location.

Other theories suggested that Atlantis is located in the Mediterranean, off the coast of Spain. It has also been argued that it could be under Antarctica. Again, there is nothing conclusive and no evidence has been cited.

I have also read comments that the whole story of Atlantis was make-believe. Perhaps loosely based on the ancient volcanic eruption that wiped out the very powerful and prideful Minoan civilisation on the island of Santorino in Greece around 1600 BC.

WHAT DID ATLANTIS LOOK LIKE?

Plato describes Atlantis as a city with three rings of water that were connected by bridges and aqueducts. Apparently there was an entrance to the south adjoining the river.

There are many artists' impressions of this great city, and it appears to have been built using sacred geometry. Atlantis has been depicted as having a super-advanced water system in the form of three concentric rings, almost like moats, surrounding the city connected by bridges – which was also described by Plato.

THE RICHAT STRUCTURE.

I had not given the location of Atlantis too much thought until my housemate, Kenzi, said to me: 'Have you ever heard of the Richat Structure in Mauritania?'

My answer was, 'No'. Then I looked it up.

The Richat Structure in Mauritania was discovered in the 1960s by astronauts, and given the nickname, the 'eye of the Sahara'. It has been proposed as the site of Atlantis.

Basically, it is a big circle in the sand – an eroded, geological dome spanning some 40 kilometers in diameter. It is an impressive circle and a very prominent feature in the Sahara Desert in Northwest Africa. You can even see it on Google maps!

Inside the structure can be found sedimentary rock in layers that appear as concentric rings – many of which have undergone hydrothermal alteration. This structure is considered to be a deeply eroded upside down dome, which overlies buried molten rock that has been hydrothermally altered. Yet what does this mean?

Well, this is where this story gets really interesting... Hydrothermal alteration is the scientific name for the process of changing one particular element, such as rock, iron, or minerals, into another form – using the conduit of water.

Metasomatism is the chemical alteration of a rock by hydrothermal processing (hot water), and other types of fluids. It is the replacement of one rock by another of different mineralogical and chemical composition. The minerals which compose the rocks are somehow dissolved and new mineral formations are deposited in their place. Plus there is BUCKETS of evidence suggesting that this was happening all the time inside the Richat Structure. Basically, crystals were being formed! Sediments such as Jasper and Quartz are found there.

There is also a different theory suggesting that the site was once an extinct volcano. However, scientific research has found that there is no shock stress in the rocks – so the debate and the mystery continues...

SKULLS!

Also found amongst the hypothermal-altered rocks, were accumulations of Acheulean archaeological artifacts. Including stone tools and quite distinctive oval and pear-shaped hand axes associated with *Homo erectus,* the species that roamed this earth over two million years ago. Furthermore, the remains of another species were found, *Homo heidelbergensis,* a race of people with a thicker jaw, indicating a meat eating/hunting culture evolving from Africa.

WHO LIVED HERE THEN?

Have we stumbled upon the ancient home of the Atlanteans and the Lemurians, who supposedly lived on a 'Lost Continent' at a much earlier period in the same general location? I feel excited by this prospect...

This conversation could go on forever, as the debate is a passionate one.
I suggest that if you are activated, do your own research. Cross-reference 'channeled' information with the archaeological evidence. The picture might paint itself for you as it did for me.

One thing is for sure – the 'eye of the Sahara' is real. She is a mystery with a story to tell that will continue to attract attention.

WHY IS THIS NOT HITTING THE NEWS?

The human mind is a curious thing. Most often there are two camps when it comes to belief or opinion. Those who believe in Faeries and those who dis-believe – UNLESS, or until, Faeries can be proven by scientific study.

So the Atlantis debate will most likely be funneled through these two camps. Plus, it is so interesting to read the online debates on the subject to notice how vehemently each one will defend their own points of view.

So for this reason alone, the passion that lies BEHIND this story indicates that there is SOMETHING still at play and alive in the story of Atlantis.

ENTER RAMTHA.

Ramtha is a dude who visits us occasionally, channeled through the body of JZ Knight. His most informative book, 'Ramtha – The White Book', tells the story of what it was like for him, living as a Lemurian in an Atlantean-ruled and dominated city. Ramtha speaks of the slavery, the mistreatment, and the lack of empathy the Atlantean race showed his race. He speaks of the advanced crystal-frequency technology and the use of water as a vibrational conduit.

RAMTHA remembers the disdain the Atlanteans had for the Lemurian race, who were passionate dancers, artists, and people of song and story. A very 'feeling' race with heart, passion and will. Short in stature and thick set in body.

The Atlanteans, on the other hand, were more advanced in the higher technologies, frequency medicine and crystal energy. They were tall and slender with light spiritual energy – advanced thinkers in their time.

What immediately comes to mind here, are my Ancient History high school lessons. I was mesmerised learning about the Minoans and Mycenaeans, who fit the above descriptions perfectly!

DEFINITELY NOTHING DEFINITE...

What matters most when we consider Atlantis (or not) is how we feel about the story. For if there is resonance, there is a remembrance, and if there is remembrance, there is a soul-thread to this time. Granted not everyone will have one. However, I certainly do and I suspect most of my readers will too.

Enjoy your own research on the matter and stay true to the beliefs and resonances felt inside your own heart. For no amount of research will ever be able to quantify that!

Giving thanks every day

FRIDAY 4th OCTOBER

Giving thanks every day

SATURDAY 5th OCTOBER

....

....

....

....

....

....

....

....

SUNDAY 6th OCTOBER

....

....

....

....

....

....

....

Giving thanks every day

MONDAY 7th OCTOBER

Giving thanks every day

TUESDAY 8th OCTOBER

....
....
....
....
....
....
....
....
....

IN THEIR HALLS OF DIAMOND, AT LAND'S END,
THEY GREW INTO AGELESS TREES, LIT WITH GEMS,
AND MASTS OF LIGHT. THEIR TOWERS WERE BRIGHT
AND TALL, AND THEIR WALLS STRONG AND MIGHTY
LIKE THE MOUNTAINS. THEIR GARDENS WERE LUSH
WITH EXOTIC PLANTS, AND THEIR ROADS
PAVED WITH SILVER AND GOLD.

J.R.R. TOLKIEN
(referencing Atlantis in "The Silmarillion")

Giving thanks every day

WEDNESDAY 9th OCTOBER

....
....
....
....
....
....
....
....
....
....
....
....
....
....
....
....
....
....

Giving thanks every day

THURSDAY 10th OCTOBER

....
....
....
....
....
....
....
....
....
....
....
....

AN HONOURING WAY TO COME TO KNOW SOMEONE
FROM ANOTHER CULTURE IS TO FIND OUT
*how they like to express gratitude
and how they like to receive it.*

KERRY HOWELLS

Giving thanks every day

FRIDAY 11th OCTOBER

Giving thanks every day

SATURDAY 12th OCTOBER

....
....
....
....
....
....
....
....

SUNDAY 13th OCTOBER

....
....
....
....
....
....
....

Giving thanks every day

MONDAY 14th OCTOBER

Giving thanks every day

....
....
....
....
....
....
....
....
....
....
....
....

IN POSEIDON'S EYES,
ATLANTIS WAS THE FAIREST OF ALL THE ISLANDS,

A PARADISE BEYOND COMPARE.

TIMAEUS BY PLATO

Giving thanks every day

WEDNESDAY 16th OCTOBER

Giving thanks every day

THURSDAY 17th OCTOBER
FULL MOON IN ARIES

How did you go with finding the balance between individual and social needs?

....

....

....

....

....

....

....

....

....

....

....

....

....

....

....

....

....

....

NH SH 17.10.24

Giving thanks every day

FRIDAY 18th OCTOBER

_____
_____
_____
_____
_____
_____
_____
_____
_____
_____
_____
_____
_____
_____
_____
_____
_____
_____
_____

Giving thanks every day

SATURDAY 19th OCTOBER

....
....
....
....
....
....
....
....
....
....

SUNDAY 20th OCTOBER

....
....
....
....
....
....
....
....

Giving thanks every day

MONDAY 21st OCTOBER

Giving thanks every day

TUESDAY 22nd OCTOBER

....
....
....
....
....
....
....
....
....
....
....
....

AND ATLANTIS SHALL RISE FROM THE WAVES...

A city shimmering with crystal and gold.

H.P. LOVECRAFT

Giving thanks every day

WEDNESDAY 23rd OCTOBER

....

....

....

....

....

....

....

....

....

....

....

....

....

....

....

....

....

....

....

....

Giving thanks every day

THURSDAY 24th OCTOBER

....

....

....

....

....

....

....

....

....

....

....

....

When we consciously practise gratitude,

WE ARE CLAIMING MORE OF

A CHOICE

IN HOW WE ACT AND SHOW UP IN THE WORLD.

KERRY HOWELLS

Giving thanks every day

FRIDAY 25th OCTOBER

Giving thanks every day

SATURDAY 26th OCTOBER

....

....

....

....

....

....

....

....

SUNDAY 27th OCTOBER

....

....

....

....

....

....

....

Giving thanks every day

MONDAY 28th OCTOBER

Giving thanks every day

TUESDAY 29th OCTOBER

....
....
....
....
....
....
....
....
....
....
....
....

BUT AS THE BLACKNESS OF NIGHT DEEPENED,
ALL THOSE WHO HAD INHABITED ATLANTIS
WERE FOREVER LOST TO THE SEA, AND THE FATE
OF THEIR CITY BECAME THE STUFF OF LEGEND.

MARION ZIMMER BRADLEY

Giving thanks every day

WEDNESDAY 30th OCTOBER

Giving thanks every day

THURSDAY 31st OCTOBER

November

S	M	T	W	T	F	S
27	28	29	30	31	1	2
3	4	5	6	7	8	9
10	11	12	13	14	15	16
17	18	19	20	21	22	23
24	25	26	27	28	29	30

IMPORTANT THINGS TO DO

....
....
....
....
....
....
....
....
....

PERSONAL GOALS

....
....
....
....
....

SEEDING MY DREAMING

....
....
....
....
....

BIRTHDAYS

....
....
....

Giving thanks every day

NEW MOON IN SCORPIO

NH SH 01.11.24

Our deepest dreams and internal longings light up with the Scorpio Sun.
Those parts of ourselves that we keep hidden from view, even from ourselves,
emerge – seeking recognition and love.

The Scorpio Moon is no stranger to secrets. She remembers all the tender revelations
you have shared with her, more perhaps than you had intended. Scorpio has a way
of drawing forth your secrets. Her understanding and charity always give you a new
perspective. It is curious how there is a strange comfort knowing that she is heard
and holds darker secrets than yours in that big chamber of a heart of hers.

This New Moon, Scorpio's planetary rulers are having an old-fashioned standoff
and you may be feeling the tension. Pluto is on the final legs of his retrograde into
Capricorn and he is pushing us to recap and remember the biggest soul lessons
that we have learnt since 2008. Opposite, over in Cancer, Mars is pushing
for emotionally honest and maturity, and emotions are running high.

The Scorpio New Moon can help us with this type of intensity. In fact, we can harness
and incorporate it as we make our intentions for the month ahead.

What are the key lessons learnt since 2008? What do you never have to do again?
Explore intentions around your inner, private realms – trust, loyalty and secrets.
How do you release anger and toxicity and process the trigger emotions?

NEW MOON
Intentions

FRIDAY 1st NOVEMBER

....

....

....

....

....

....

....

Trust issues... What are yours?

Can you heal them?

SCORPIO

♏

MIND

....
....
....
....
....
....

BODY

....
....
....
....
....

SPIRIT

....
....
....
....
....

SOUL

....
....
....
....
....

Giving thanks every day

SATURDAY 2nd NOVEMBER

....
....
....
....
....
....
....
....

SUNDAY 3rd NOVEMBER

....
....
....
....
....
....
....
....

Causal Emotions

I love BOOKS! I am constantly treating myself to a new one at a bookstore, or picking up old and tattered ones at garage sales. I keep them everywhere – in every room in the house. Most of the books on my bookshelf I have not read. Plus the ones I have read, if they are good enough, are given away to others who need to read them.

Francis Power once said; 'Knowledge is power'. Sometimes, I worry that if all books eventually become digital, what's to stop the mysterious editing of such files. The missing chapter, or the relevant prelude, or the acknowledgements ... The original source of the information?

I know there are seed banks being built all over the world, but perhaps we need to be creating book safes: to keep safe all knowledge that presently exists in the physical printed form. For after all, books tell stories, and inside the stories is a map of our past from which the future is created.

This is a very long prelude to the conversation about causal emotions.

When I began my healing journey and exploration into healing pathways, I knew intimately that my emotional body was in overload, or overwhelm mode.

The era of 'create your own reality' was very much in fashion. Gurus and spiritual way-showers, such as Louise Hay and Anthony Robbins, were promoting the power of positive thinking and manifesting change through will-power. Movies and documentary films such as 'The Secret' were supporting the belief that miracles happen and all you need to do is be open to them. However, none of these teachings worked for me. In fact, none of these methods made a shit of difference in the healing of my chronic fatigue and the health issues that accompanied this.

I just KNEW that when it came to my healing journey, I was missing a vital piece of knowledge.

Enter AJ Miller. It was the year 2000. I had made some important lifestyle and spiritual decisions, which included not getting married and following a more INFORMED PATH. I decided that I would ALLOW GUIDANCE and therefore, GRACE, TO DIRECT MY COURSE.

It was around this time, my dear friend Maggie gave me a DVD and said; 'This may help you on your journey'. I watched a presentation given by AJ (Alan John Miller) called: 'Causal Emotions'. I could not move away from the screen. It was the information I had been looking for.

AJ is a pioneer and advocate for the emotional body. He teaches that in today's society we have mostly become emotionally suppressed. He explains that a child will carry the subconscious behavioural patterns of the mother (passed on in utero) and also from the family household during the process of growing up. This theory rang so true for me! I was emotionally suppressed and I really had no clue as to who I was, or what was important and true for me. What WAS the song in my soul? I'd only ever lived following the expectations of family, friends and society.

THE SACRED FEMININE

I've always been a Magdalene fan – always believed the scenario that Mary was way more than a disciple of Christ; and that she was, in fact, his counterpart. Christ's equal. But the narrative had been set. Mary was a lowly whore and Jesus took mercy on her. I KNEW that the truth of this relationship was distorted. I also knew that, somehow, this was related to the suppression of emotions on this planet. The truth of the feminine was hidden, and therefore so was her power.

I understand and relate to the Feminine 'feeling realm'. Which is balanced by the more Masculine 'mental realm' in conversation with the Feminine 'soul' and the Masculine 'spirit'. It's a foursome!

So, when I stumbled across the causal emotions, my deeply suppressed feminine essence was activated like a volcano.

CAUSAL EMOTIONS

Live in your soul. There are causal emotions that are sometimes carried forward, across the placenta, from your grandmother to your mother, and on to you. These emotions are the elusive ones, that niggle and scratch at your window; you can hear them, but you can't see them. You want so much to let them in, but you have no idea what they even are!!

Will they hurt you, can you be with them, or even worse, will they kill you? Will you survive them? It's a deep underwater well – an unseen terrain where you have not consciously gone. These are the causal emotions.

The good news is that they are just energy.

Plus knowledge is power, so here is some knowledge:

There are five causal emotions:
1. Love
2. Fear
3. Anger
4. Grief
5. Shame

Get to know these creatures, for these are the colours of your rainbow that live eternally in your soul. Any level of suppression of these energies, will ultimately dim the light that is you.

HOW TO PROCESS CAUSAL EMOTIONS

It is causal emotions that drive the TRIGGERS in your life. It's not the person, the situation or the climate – it is the emotion (that dwells deep). Gracefully, God has created a system called the LAW OF ATTRACTION, that will deliver your soul with the exact frequency you need to process what lies beneath. The bigger the trigger, the bigger the energy (emotion) that is being held under water.

The fastest way to process casual emotion is to know without doubt that everything you feel is YOU. Once you can take full responsibility for what you are feeling, then, you will process and transmute the energy back to love.

BUT HOW CAN I FEEL GRATEFUL WHEN I FEEL SO RESENTFUL?

My dear friend and mentor, Kerry Howells, wrote an award-winning book addressing this question. It's called; *'Untangling you: How can I be grateful when I feel so resentful?'*. To find out more go to kerryhowells.com.

Ultimately, when you understand that all triggers are designed to enlighten your soul to wholeness, you will begin to welcome them in.

I remember my 30s, when I was triggered all the time and constantly ANGRY. And, I created relationships to fuel that anger. In my 40s I was very sad. Again, my relationships mirrored my state. Now in my 50s, I'm starting to sniff out causal emotions that need to be healed. I know that ultimately my relationships will activate that pathway, light it up like a Christmas tree, and for that I am grateful.

JUDGEMENT

Look, just don't do it. Judging others is the same as dumping your bags of rubbish in someone else's back yard because they deserve it. Judging others is a cop out.
It is an avoidance strategy, a 'thing' you have learned to do in order to avoid your own causal emotions.

If you are judging someone, ask yourself these three questions:

1. What am I seeing in this person that I do not like?
2. Where is that in myself AND how does it show up?
3. Can I take ownership for this energy in my own soul?

If you CAN NOT ask yourselves these questions, you may be suffering from the causal emotion of shame. Which is the emotion that lies at the very depth of your ocean. Where it is pitch black...

PRAYER

If you decide to get serious about your Karma and want to live your life with a clean slate, prayer will support your journey back to a balanced state.

Ask your creator, in a sacred tone; 'How can I gain access to that which I cannot feel? Can you please help me to own, integrate and therefore heal that which is not yet resolved'.

And if you do this sincerely, you will be given a trigger to work with.

My beloved teacher and friend, Ramtha, calls these triggers 'runners'. And believe it or not, his students feel BLESSED to be given these difficult life circumstances so that they may heal, and therefore grow.

Giving thanks every day

MONDAY 4th NOVEMBER

Giving thanks every day

TUESDAY 5th NOVEMBER

....
....
....
....
....
....
....
....
....
....
....
....
....
....

In the vast ocean of emotions,

WE NAVIGATE THE TIDES OF HAPPINESS, SADNESS, ANGER, AND LOVE, FOREVER AWASH

IN THE EBB AND FLOW OF LIFE.

Giving thanks every day

WEDNESDAY 6th NOVEMBER

....
....
....
....
....
....
....
....
....
....
....
....
....
....
....
....
....
....

Giving thanks every day

THURSDAY 7th NOVEMBER

....

....

....

....

....

....

....

....

....

....

....

....

....

Feelings, like water, can be gentle and soothing, or they can be powerful and overwhelming.

Giving thanks every day

FRIDAY 8th NOVEMBER

Giving thanks every day

SATURDAY 9th NOVEMBER

....
....
....
....
....
....
....
....

SUNDAY 10th NOVEMBER

....
....
....
....
....
....
....

Giving thanks every day

MONDAY 11th NOVEMBER

Giving thanks every day

TUESDAY 12th NOVEMBER

....
....
....
....
....
....
....
....
....
....
....
....

JUST AS A LAKE REFLECTS THE BEAUTY AROUND IT,
OUR FEELINGS MIRROR THE WORLD WITHIN US.

Giving thanks every day

WEDNESDAY 13th NOVEMBER

Giving thanks every day

....

....

....

....

....

....

....

....

....

....

....

....

TEARS
are the liquid expression of emotions too deep for words, a release that cleanses and nourishes the soul.

Giving thanks every day

FRIDAY 15th NOVEMBER

Giving thanks every day

SATURDAY 16th & SUNDAY 17th NOVEMBER
FULL MOON IN TAURUS

How are your intentions coming to fruition?

....
....
....
....
....
....
....
....
....
....
....
....
....
....
....
....
....
....
....
....

Giving thanks every day

MONDAY 18th NOVEMBER

Giving thanks every day

TUESDAY 19th NOVEMBER

....
....
....
....
....
....
....
....
....
....
....

E-motions are energy in motion.

IF THEY ARE NOT EXPRESSED, THE ENERGY
IS REPRESSED. AS ENERGY IT HAS TO GO
SOMEWHERE. EMOTIONAL ENERGY MOVES US AS
DOES ALL ENERGY... TO DENY EMOTION IS TO DENY
THE GROUND AND VITAL ENERGY OF OUR LIFE.

Giving thanks every day

WEDNESDAY 20th NOVEMBER

Giving thanks every day

THURSDAY 21st NOVEMBER

....
....
....
....
....
....
....
....
....
....
....
....

Gratitude is the sign of noble souls.

AESOP

Giving thanks every day

FRIDAY 22nd NOVEMBER

Giving thanks every day

SATURDAY 23rd NOVEMBER

....
....
....
....
....
....
....
....

SUNDAY 24th NOVEMBER

....
....
....
....
....
....
....

Giving thanks every day

MONDAY 25th NOVEMBER

Giving thanks every day

TUESDAY 26th NOVEMBER

....
....
....
....
....
....
....
....
....
....
....
....

DEEPLY ACCEPT HOW THINGS ARE RIGHT NOW.

Giving thanks every day

WEDNESDAY 27th NOVEMBER

Giving thanks every day

THURSDAY 28th NOVEMBER

Giving thanks every day

FRIDAY 29th NOVEMBER

....

....

....

NEW MOON IN SAGITTARIUS

NH SH 01.12.24

The Sun returns to Sagittarius, kindling enthusiasm
and generating that grand mood that ANYTHING may be possible.

This New Moon in Sagittarius is open to hearing the call of the wild
and winding road. Let that kindling spark of optimism grow.
Venture forth, find your quest and know that it is *your* destiny that you seek to fulfil.

Directly across from this New Moon, we find Jupiter (the ruling planet of Sagittarius)
in chatty and multi-focused Gemini. No topic is off the table. Conversations
go longform and the merit of every idea is up for debate – no sentimentality here.
We are after capital letter TRUTH. There is so much to explore – and as Mercury
is currently retrograde, certain histories may be due for a revision.

Saturn in Pisces is holding court with a hard square to the New Moon and Jupiter.
He is keeping our feet on the ground and reminding us that just because
we can think it, does not mean it manifests in reality. Yet!

That said – this is the time to place seriously big, grand intentions around
life direction, study, travel and career goals. First we dream it, then we manifest it.
You will be laying a solid foundation if you can incorporate even a touch of Saturn's
practical intelligence and know-how in your intentions.

NEW MOON
Intentions

SUNDAY 1st DECEMBER

....

....

....

....

....

....

....

First we dream it, then we manifest it.

What is IT?

SAGITTARIUS

MIND

....

....

....

....

BODY

....

....

....

SPIRIT

....

....

....

SOUL

....

....

....

....

December

S	M	T	W	T	F	S
1	2	3	4	5	6	7
8	9	10	11	12	13	14
15	16	17	18	19	20	21
22	23	24	25	26	27	28
29	30	31	1	2	3	4

IMPORTANT THINGS TO DO

PERSONAL GOALS

SEEDING MY DREAMING

BIRTHDAYS

Whales...

THE SENTINELS OF SOUND

This has perhaps been the most difficult article to write in this Diary. I've been contemplating it for months... what to share with you that hasn't already been said about this magnificent creature.

Finally, at the eleventh hour, the answer dropped in. I was in the dog park throwing a ball to my cavoodle and my labrador when the answer came... to just share my experiences.

I'll start with Noah, the cavoodle. He's my newly adopted puppy – a rehome from my neighbour who was unable to keep him. Whilst he is gorgeous, Noah is also NAUGHTY! Crazy stuff like jumping on kitchen benches, biting my bum, freaking out at the sound of a bird, high-pitched barking in the middle of the night... I really did doubt my capacity to train this little wayward pup.

Yet, over time, a special thing happened. I started communicating with him in the dog park with sounds. Because he is a little dog with a high-pitched voice, I tried to match his pitch. It was also the only way I could communicate with him as he would run SO far away!

As he ran and chased the ball, I'd make a high-pitched, 'Weeeeee' sound – meaning, 'This is fun'. If he ran away, I'd make a different, 'Uh oh' sound – meaning, 'Come back'. If he tried to dig under the fence and escape, I'd make another noise like a sharp horn – meaning, 'Warning, that is dangerous'.

Over a short amount of time, Noah and I had a communication system going, based on frequency. He knew exactly what my sounds were communicating; I no longer needed words.

And this is the wisdom that whales carry. Only on a much more intricate level. If I go out on an intuitive limb, I suspect that whales carry the frequency codes of language, a code that has been in existence since the beginning of consciousness.

They knew about emotions, culture, love, pain, suffering, hope, joy and connection... long before we did.

Humans are only now understanding that everything is frequency and tone. You can experiment with this if you have a pet – or a partner! Rather than use words, see if you can communicate using sound. It will either be a positive or negative sound in a major or minor key. The sound frequency will be sharp and pointy or long and low.

WHALES ARE SENTIENT!

In Buddhism, the definition of 'sentient being' v **every conscious creature.**
This is defined as the ability to feel pain. All animals are sentient. Although it appears some are MORE SO than others. (At least that's what I believe.)

Whales have a strong SOCIAL CULTURE. They hunt krill en masse and are able to organise their very specific hunting strategy through communicating with clicks and other sounds. What's even more amazing is that they know exactly where the fish will be at a specific time.

This wisdom is handed down, through generations. Training lasts for at least three years through the intimate attachment and love between the mother and calf.

The Sentience Institute, a nonprofit, interdisciplinary think tank researching long-term social and technological change, puts forward the idea that sentience is simply the ability to have both positive and negative experiences. This tells me that animal brains are similar to human brains – when both sides of the brain are used in a balanced way, a unified field is created.

UNITY CONSCIOUS

Unity consciousness is something I bang on about a lot. It is the understanding that as a species, we are all connected. Separation is simply a disease of the mind. The whales know and LIVE this truth – their motivation is always for their family and clan. Their care extends way beyond their sense of self, for they know that their own mortality depends on this truth.

AND THEN ONE DAY...

I had made some core decisions on how to live my life. Admittedly, this was on the back of my own mid-life crisis. It was the year I began to write about gratitude and the gifts of this practice. About 15 minutes after making the decision to work in a unified field, I sat on my verandah and a whale breached out of the ocean. It was as if this whale somehow felt my conviction and danced just for me. It was a validation. This moment further cemented my conviction that separation is illusionary.

As if on cue, it happened again! This beauty, the breaching whale, showed me what was possible when I live in a way that CONSIDERS connection to others on a moment-by-moment basis. She validated the fact that miracles are possible when we all remember this simple truth. You can read more of this story at: givingthanks.co/about

BEFORE THE BREACH...

I had never really thought much about whales until I moved to Byron Bay. My first introduction to whales was stumbling across what used to be an old whaling station, which had been closed down in 1962, just eight years after it opened. The whale building was a great big, grand old shed beside the beach. From there, whalers in their boats would go into the bay, harpoon whales and drag them back to be butchered. The whales were killed for their oil which provided fuel.

After the closure of the whaling station, the sheds were abandoned, so the local Byronians renamed the location as 'The Epicentre'. We would gather there to celebrate, in dance, at big community doof parties. There's something really eerie about being inside an old whaling shed; yet, dancing there all night under a full moon was also amazing. Something incredibly healing was taking place. Just by being there and standing in the room, realising that these incredible mammals, these largest beings of our oceans, had been pulled into this shed and sacrificed. It was a jolt to my senses and a light bulb went on in my mind and heart. This cannot happen any more!

Years later I came across a beautiful man, Dave Clayton, who took people out on his catamaran to swim with the whales. My first whale sighting was phenomenal! To be that close to a living breathing whale, three times the size of the boat we were on, was absolutely amazing. Reverence is the only way I can describe what I felt. Surges of energy and excitement rippled through my body when I neared the whale. Without having studied the science, I knew that these creatures are extremely special and hold a frequency that is really REALLY important for the stability of this planet.

I was so excited when a whale came up to the boat – I jumped in the water! There I was with my snorkel, mask and flippers just three metres away from a whale!!! Apparently that's dangerous and also illegal to get close to the whales these days. It was a different era–less regulated–and I knew the whale did not mind at all!

So, I'm in the water, drifting in the current of the ocean with the whale and I felt completely safe. I knew he wasn't going to hurt me and I also knew that he was aware that I was there. What's even more beautiful is that the whales we encountered came to the boat from afar – they came to say hello. They were so friendly and open, and extremely curious–not afraid at all, their hearts open, wanting to connect with us. And that in itself is profound.

AUSTRALIA'S WHALING HISTORY

Whaling in Australia began in the late 18th century. Just for the record there is no known history of Aboriginal communities in Australia hunting whales.

Whale blubber was melted down to be used as oil for lamp fuel, lubricants and candles as well as a base for perfumes and soaps. Whale bone was used to make corsets, whips and umbrellas. Whaling and the export of whale oil and other bioproducts became one of Australia's first primary industries.

Eventually, kerosene, petroleum, and other fossil fuels became much more popular and reliable than whale oil and, therefore, the industry plummeted. Sadly, whale numbers diminished from all the hunting and, by the early 1970s, several species of whales were listed as endangered. While some species are showing signs of recovery, whales are slow breeding and long-lived. They also face many threats today including ocean noise pollution, commercial whaling, ship strikes, pollution (notably plastic pollution), entanglement in fishing gear and environmental changes due to climate change.

FACTS ABOUT WHALES

Whales are the largest mammals on Earth. They breathe air, nurse their young with milk, and have warm blood. Some species, like the blue whale, filter feed on tiny shrimp-like animals called krill, while others, like orcas (killer whales), are formidable predators that hunt fish, seals, and even other whales. They are highly intelligent creatures with complex social structures. They communicate using a range of vocalisations, including songs, clicks, and whistles. Did you know that killer whales are actually dolphins? Another interesting fact is that whales are the only known mammals, apart from humans, to experience menopause

WHALE MENOPAUSE

Female whales, particularly certain species such as killer whales and short-finned pilot whales, go through menopause. This means they stop reproducing at a certain age but continue to live for many years, providing valuable knowledge and guidance to their pod. The reasons for menopause in whales are not fully understood, but some theories suggest that older females help to ensure the survival of their offspring and their pod by helping with foraging, by protecting the group from predators, and through sharing their knowledge of migration routes and food sources.

THE VITAL ROLE WHALES PLAY IN REGULATING OUR OCEANS ECOSYSTEMS

Whales stir up nutrients from the depths below when they dive deep into the ocean – promoting nutrient circulation. These nutrients support phytoplankton on the surface of the water, which is a major food source for many fish and crustaceans. Whale faeces also provide nutrients for the plants and phytoplankton to grow, which in turn absorb carbon dioxide from the Earth's atmosphere and contribute to around 50 percent of the world's oxygen!

WHALE STRANDINGS

Also known as whale beachings, whale strandings are not fully understood. Two years ago over 200 whales beached themselves on the shores near Strahan on the west coast of Tasmania. Multiple theories exist to explain WHY whales strand themselves, but I don't believe we fully understand the reasons. Theories include: illness and injury; environmental factors such as rapidly changing water temperatures; that following a stranded member of a pod could lead to mass strandings; and possible navigation errors. Whales rely on the Earth's magnetic fields, sonar, and other navigational cues to navigate. Abnormalities caused by changes in the earth's magnetic field and noise pollution may interfere with a whale's biological navigation causing it to lose its sense of direction. You can find out more at: seashepherd.org.au

IN CLOSING

Writing this piece has opened the door to my heart and I'm now wanting to do MORE, to understand more and connect with the whales more often.

There is a movie called 'Whale Rider'–about a young Māori woman who actually rides on the back of a whale...

Watch it.
Let it activate you.

My challenge
to you...
Should you choose to play
Meet a whale...
Make a connection.
Soon!

Giving thanks every day

MONDAY 2nd DECEMBER

Giving thanks every day

TUESDAY 3rd DECEMBER

WE DO NOT INHERIT THE EARTH FROM OUR ANCESTORS;

WE BORROW IT FROM OUR CHILDREN.

NATIVE AMERICAN PROVERB

Giving thanks every day

WEDNESDAY 4th DECEMBER

Giving thanks every day

THURSDAY 5th DECEMBER

....
....
....
....
....
....
....
....
....
....
....
....

The whale is the embodiment of
MAGNIFICENCE IN NATURE.

CAPTAIN CHARLES MELVILLE SCAMMON

Giving thanks every day

FRIDAY 6th DECEMBER

Giving thanks every day

SATURDAY 7th DECEMBER

....
....
....
....
....
....
....
....

SUNDAY 8th DECEMBER

....
....
....
....
....
....

Giving thanks every day

MONDAY 9th DECEMBER

Giving thanks every day

TUESDAY 10th DECEMBER

....

....

....

....

....

....

....

....

....

....

....

THE WHALE IS A CREATURE OF THE WILDEST POWER.

HENRY DAVID THOREAU

Giving thanks every day

WEDNESDAY 11th DECEMBER

....

....

....

....

....

....

....

....

....

....

....

....

....

....

....

....

....

....

....

....

Giving thanks every day

THURSDAY 12th DECEMBER

....

....

....

....

....

....

....

....

....

....

....

....

The whale is nature's masterpiece.

HERMAN MELVILLE

Giving thanks every day

FRIDAY 13th DECEMBER

Giving thanks every day

SATURDAY 14th & SUNDAY 15th DECEMBER
FULL MOON IN GEMINI

How are your intentions coming to fruition?

....

....

....

....

....

....

....

....

....

....

....

....

....

....

....

....

....

....

NH SH 15.12.24

Giving thanks every day

MONDAY 16th DECEMBER

Giving thanks every day

TUESDAY 17th DECEMBER

....
....
....
....
....
....
....
....
....
....
....
....

WHEN WE ARE GRATEFUL,

WE ARE GRACEFUL.

Giving thanks every day

WEDNESDAY 18th DECEMBER

Giving thanks every day

THURSDAY 19th DECEMBER

Giving thanks every day

FRIDAY 20th DECEMBER

Giving thanks every day

SATURDAY 21st DECEMBER

....
....
....
....
....
....
....
....

SUNDAY 22nd DECEMBER

....
....
....
....
....
....
....

Giving thanks every day

MONDAY 23rd DECEMBER

Giving thanks every day

TUESDAY 24th DECEMBER

....
....
....
....
....
....
....
....
....
....
....
....

GRATITUDE IS NOT JUST ABOUT GIVING THANKS
FOR WHAT IS GOING WELL...
IT IS A DEEP ACCEPTANCE AND HONOURING
OF WHAT IS HERE IN THIS PRESENT MOMENT.

Giving thanks every day

WEDNESDAY 25th DECEMBER

....
....
....
....
....
....
....
....
....
....
....
....
....
....
....
....
....
....

Giving thanks every day

THURSDAY 26th DECEMBER

Giving thanks every day
FRIDAY 27th DECEMBER

Giving thanks every day

SATURDAY 28th DECEMBER

....

....

....

....

....

....

....

....

SUNDAY 29th DECEMBER

....

....

....

....

....

....

....

Giving thanks every day

MONDAY 30th DECEMBER

....

....

....

NEW MOON IN CAPRICORN

NH 30.12.24 SH 31.12.24

As we stand at the cusp of a whole new, shiny year, we look back at what we've achieved in 2024. What cliff face did you scale this year? What view do you see as you look back over the landscape of the year? When the Moon is in Capricorn she shares with us an emotionally-contained, pragmatic mood. She dries out illusions and hysteria making it easier to see the bones of any given situation and helps us to grasp what is most important.

Sounds so serious! What about the party? What about celebrations? Well! Mars in Leo is sending a joyful trine to the North Node in Aries, encouraging us to step into the future with confidence and flair. Mercury in Sagittarius trines Chiron in Aries, suggesting conversations for some will take on a positive and healing tone, while others will be spitting their words out like fireballs – truths will be spoken either way. Neptune in Pisces opposes the South Node in the early degrees of Aquarius – expect some nostalgia as you get pulled down memory lane or receive a blast from the past in the form of an unexpected encounter. How are you going to weave these energies into your New Moon intentions?

The ever-grounded, no nonsense qualities of the Capricorn Moon will help you see what's truly important. She'll advise you on what you need to do to accomplish the upcoming months' (and possibly the year's) mission. Just tune in and note it all down

NEW MOON
Intentions

TUESDAY 31st DECEMBER

....

....

....

....

....

....

....

What was truly important for you in 2024?

Reflect...

CAPRICORN